NURSING AND HAND REARING NEWBORN PUPPIES

by Betty Bloomfield

Nursing and Hand Rearing Newborn Puppies

Copyright © Betty Bloomfield 1994

ISBN 0907616 93 3

Original issue sponsored by Hill's Pet Nutrition Ltd.

All rights reserved

Reprinted in 2005

Published by:

Able Publishing
13 Station Road
Knebworth
Herts SG3 6AP

Tel: 01438 814316 / 812320
Fax: 01438 815232

Email: books@ablepublishing.co.uk
Website: www.ablepublishing.co.uk

To the Memory of

Dee-Dee

A Little Sheltie

Who by winning the battle for her own life indirectly gave life to so many

Betty brought Dee-Dee, the sole survivor of five puppies, through her puppyhood against all the odds to live a happy life until she was fifteen. This gave Betty the inspiration for The Puppy & Kitten Clinic.

THE PUPPY & KITTEN CLINIC

Patron: The Princesses Antoinette of Monaco

SPECIAL CARE NURSING FOR NEW BORN PUPPIES AND KITTENS

(up to 3-4 weeks of age)

Specialised Nursing with Veterinary Consultation for orphaned, preterm caesarian, fading, weak or small puppies and kittens unable to feed.

All treatment is under the supervision of the Clinic's Veterinary Surgeon.

Mrs Betty Bloomfield

Publisher's Note:
The Puppy & Kitten Clinic is no longer in existence. Demand for this book continues, however, and we have therefore undertaken to reproduce it as closely to the original as possible.

ACKNOWLEDGMENTS

Betty Bloomfield is a dedicated animal lover. I began to appreciate her vast skill and knowledge when she nursed my badly bitten, three day old puppy, who was limp and in severe shock, back to full health. In this book on hand rearing, Betty Bloomfield shares some of her ideas and knowledge, drawn from a lifetime spent with dogs, from her experience as a nurse (including working on a special care baby unit), as a dog breeder, in dog obedience training, taking her Border Collie "Maggie" from beginners to Championship "C" and as a mother. She constantly devotes unlimited time to give these puppies and kittens, those capable of leading a normal life, the chance to survive.

Adrienne Hughes

"This book is a testimony to one woman's dedication to the nursing care of newborn puppies that would otherwise face certain death. It is our hope that by making the publication of this book possible, Betty Bloomfield's life long experience and practical approach can be transferred to many other would be carers, who lack only the knowledge Betty has gained, to be able to save many more of these tiny lives."

Graham Milligan. MA VetMB MRCVS
U K Commercial Manager
Hill's Pet Nutrition Ltd.

FOREWORD

When Betty Bloomfield asked me to write the foreword for this book, I felt very honoured. Since I first met Betty, I have never ceased to admire her endless patience and commitment to raising neonates. Anyone who has ever attempted to rear newborn puppies and kittens will appreciate the enormous challenge of having anything up to 15 neonates to care for. It is a 24 hour a day commitment for 365 days a year. Betty has had no help since her daughter, Samantha, started at University but, despite this and not a single night's uninterrupted sleep, Betty is always enthusiastic about her vocation and I have never seen her veer from her absolute concern and dedication to each of her charges. Few of Betty's 'patients' are normal healthy puppies and kittens. Most have undergone some early trauma; some are premature, some have lost their dam during caesarean section and many others have been fed inappropriate foods by misguided well-wishers. As well as the stress of the loss of their natural mother, some of Betty's charges have physical handicaps to cope with, for example, cleft palates and flat chests, and others have been under veterinary care for bacterial and viral infections. The challenge is enormous. Betty has had her share of disappointments but she has saved hundreds of puppies and kittens any less dedicated individual would have lost.

Premature, orphaned and sick puppies and kittens and those with special needs all arrive at Betty's Hertfordshire clinic and each is given her expertise in hand rearing with love and dedication. A bedroom of Betty's house has been refurbished as a puppy and kitten ward and the neonatal 'patients' are housed in specially adapted incubators. Most stay with her for 3 to 4 weeks. Once Betty is satisfied that the puppies/kittens and their owners can cope, they return home. A few stay longer; some for treatment and others are abandoned at the clinic by their owners or given to the clinic and await new homes. A few animals never leave; Horris, a Persian cat who had a cleft palate, and Muppett, a Shetland Sheepdog, have a permanent home with Betty. Other ex-patients visit her. One of these is Kym who arrived at Betty's home 4 years ago as an abandoned sickly pup weighing less than one ounce and is now a bouncy middle aged terrier who has to watch her waist line. Betty's photograph album is full of similar stories.

Betty is a nurse and, during her career, worked in a special care baby unit. This experience has greatly benefited the clinic. Betty is also building up a library on small animal paediatric literature and has a special interest in the nutrition of neonates. Breeders and veterinary surgeons are not infrequently faced with the dilemma of what to do with a litter of orphaned or needy puppies or kittens. Many owners do not have the expertise to successfully rear orphans and veterinary staff rarely have enough time to dedicate to the rearing of neonates. And that is where Betty can help. But there are too few "Bettys" and many owners have had no option but to try to "go-it-alone", often in the dark. With the encouragement of Hill's Pet Products and many friends, clients and veterinary surgeons, Betty has written this guide. It aims to help dedicated pet owners and breeders rear their orphaned or needy puppies and to help them recognise health problems. Many hundreds of puppies and kittens have passed through Betty's clinic since it started on very modest grounds in 1972 and the advise and guidance set out in this book is based on her considerable experience. Much is still to be learnt about canine and feline paediatrics but, hopefully, with more veterinary interest and investigation into the problems of neonates and with practical advice from Betty, fewer newborn animals will be needlessly lost. I, for one, am very grateful to Betty for putting her experience and expertise in this field on paper.

Sarah Wilkins BVSc MRCVS
6th November 1993

CONTENTS

INTRODUCTION

Puppies may need to be hand reared either because their dam is unable to feed her puppies herself, or because a puppy is unable to thrive satisfactorily in the nest. There remains great concern amongst many veterinary surgeons and breeders, that by rearing weak or sick puppies many will grow into weak, sickly adults. This has not been the experience at the Puppy and Kitten Clinic. The hundreds of puppies that have been reared at the Clinic since 1974 have shown that a setback early in a puppy's life need not prevent a puppy attaining its full potential to grow into a strong, healthy dog.

The Clinic has always believed that there can be no justification for rearing any puppy that will not be able to live a full and active life as an adult. We have always taken great care to assess the POTENTIAL QUALITY OF LIFE of every puppy we have reared. This should always be the primary consideration as to whether hand rearing should be attempted. It is vital that anyone rearing very sick puppies is able to assess the condition of a puppy accurately. All puppies must be reviewed regularly until they make a full recovery, die or are euthanased. If a puppy has a deformity its prognosis should be discussed with a veterinary surgeon.

With animals, like dogs, which have multiple births, abnormal or deformed embryos are not normally aborted during pregnancy. Some embryos are absorbed *in utero*. However a number of puppies will be born dead or with little chance of survival. However the experience of the Clinic has been that breeders need not accept the current estimated loss, of between 10 and 15 of full term neonatal puppies, as the norm. Some of the factors that effect mortality include the care the dam and the puppies receive, the breed of the puppy and the selection of the specific breeding stock.

It is hoped that by sharing the knowledge gained at the Clinic more breeders will be able to have greater success when they hand rear puppies. However, very weak or sick puppies frequently need specialist intensive nursing if they are to have a chance of survival. It is unrealistic to expect all veterinary surgeons to have a specific interest in the care of neonatal puppies or to have the specialised staff and facilities necessary to save sick neonates. You may have to search hard to find such help. Puppies continue to be referred to this Clinic from all over the country by both veterinary surgeons and breeders, because suitable help cannot be found locally.

The treatment of neonatal puppies cannot be compared with that of human babies. There is usually a financial limitation on the cost of treatment to an individual puppy and research published in this field is sparse. The small size of very young puppies can make their treatment problematic and routine procedures like taking a blood sample are often difficult. Despite this, improved veterinary knowledge and an increased understanding of how to care for neonates gives the potential to save many more puppies than at present.

The Clinic is very proud of all the puppies it has reared some of which have become Show Champions, as adults. However, every puppy that is reared to full health and placed in a caring and permanent home justifies all the hard work that is involved. These dogs invariably have a special affinity with humans. Contrary to popular belief the hand reared bitch puppies are usually excellent mothers themselves, but it is very important to identify those dogs who may have hereditary problems to ensure these animals are not used for breeding.

CHAPTER ONE

PUPPY DEVELOPMENT

CONTENTS

PUPPY DEVELOPMENT

Many puppies die or require hand rearing because they do not receive suitable care. There is tremendous potential to save more puppies by providing care that is more appropriate to their needs. Success of hand rearing is greatly increased if a puppy receives care that keeps all physical stresses to a minimum. The needs of a puppy vary as it develops, so it is important that the care given to the puppy is adjusted accordingly.

Different breeds develop at slightly different rates and there can be considerable variation between individual puppies. Illness will slow down normal development and limit the way a puppy learns as it is denied many of the normal experiences of a litter reared by its dam. However, when they recover these puppies should catch up their peers.

Puppy development can be divided into four stages:

i) Neonatal - during the first two weeks of life
ii) Transitional - between 14-21 days of age
iii) Socialisation - between 3-12 weeks of age
iv) Juvenile - from 3-12 months of age

Neonatal Period 0-14 days

Puppies are born in a very care dependent state. Most of the body systems are at an early stage of development, and so they are often unable of function adequately if put under stress. The first 36 hours of life are the most critical for a puppy's survival.

General Condition

Puppies may appear scraggy when born, but they should fill out rapidly within 24hours of birth. Healthy puppies sleep for most of the time, and apart from occasional twitching appear relaxed. When woken puppies should search vigorously for a teat to suck.

Crying

Puppies do not cry without reason. They can feel pain from the time of birth, and also cry if they are too hot, too cold or hungry.

Although the cry of the puppy should be strong, the puppy cannot move away from a painful stimulus easily as it can only wriggle from side to side. Always look for the cause of a puppy crying, and rectify the problem as soon as possible, to prevent the puppy becoming exhausted.

Body Temperature

At birth a puppy has no control of its own body temperature which should be between 35.5°-36°C (96°-97°F). The puppy is totally dependent on its environment to maintain the correct temperature. If a puppy becomes cold it may cry, but if the situation is not rectified, the puppy will become quiet and can quickly develop hypothermia. This is a common cause of death in young puppies. Hyperthermia occurs if a puppy becomes too hot, and this can induce shock. This condition can also be fatal.

Touch

This is well developed at birth. Puppies like something soft to nestle up to, to sleep. Puppies benefit from gentle daily handling e.g. when weighed and fed as this lays the foundation of human socialisation.

Sight

The eyelids of a puppy should be fused at birth. Puppies born with their eyes open seldom survive. Normally, the eyes start to open between 10-14 days of age. All puppies' eyes are blue when they first open.

Smell

Puppies are able to smell when born enabling them to home in on a teat.

Hearing

A puppy is born deaf and the ears appear lifeless. In most breeds the ear canal begins to open between 6-14 days of age.

Digestion

Puppies are born with a good sense of taste. They should have a strong suck reflex which is developed before the puppy is born. The stomach of a young puppy is very small. In a puppy of a toy breed it is about the size of a wren's egg so it can only hold a small quantity of feed. This means the puppy needs frequent, regular feeds. A puppy cannot survive for long without fluid.

A **healthy puppy** normally doubles its birth weight in 7-10 days after birth. This rapid rate of growth is achieved by the rich quality of the bitches' milk.

Puppies require stimulation to pass both urine and faeces. In the nest, this is provided by the dam licking the genital and anal areas. The first excretion or meconium is the waste products that have accumulated whilst the puppy was in the uterus. This is usually a firm, dark tarry texture. The early faeces of a puppy should be of a toothpaste consistency, and are normally rather granular in texture and a fairly bright yellow colour. The colour gradually changes to a yellowish brown.

Mobility

At birth puppies can move all four limbs, and can travel a short distance by wriggling from side to side. They will search out the mammary area or something warm to nestle into, but they cannot travel far as they tire quickly. Puppies should start walking when 10-14 days old.

Transitional Stage 14-21 days

This is a time when puppies become more aware of their environment.

General Condition

The puppies continue to grow at a rapid rate and should appear filled out and sleek. They spend less time sleeping and so are able to start exploring their immediate surroundings.

By this stage they are able to locate the source of pain and to move away from it.

Body Temperature

Increasingly, a puppy is able to control its body temperature which by now should be 36.5°-37°C (96°-98°F). They are still dependent on being nursed in a warm environment and can still easily become too cold or too hot.

Sight

The puppy can gradually begin to focus its eyes. It will try and avoid bright light. Keep puppies away from bright lights.

Hearing

By two weeks puppies begin orientating towards a sound. The ears are usually fully open by 17 days of age.

Digestion

Milk remains the main source of food. Digestion creates warmth. By two weeks of age a puppy has developed its cough reflex. Most puppies can start to lap by 2½ weeks.

By about 18 days a puppy will be able to excrete without being stimulated, and will usually choose to do so in a corner of its box.

Movement

By two weeks the puppy's muscles should be strong enough to take the puppy's weight enabling it to walk. **Note** – Beware of puppies becoming too heavy and thus unable to stand and/or support their own weight.

Socialisation Stage 3-12 weeks

This is a time of rapid development during which puppies learn to adapt to independent life. Careful socialisation with people and dogs is important. Puppies should be exposed gradually to normal household activities e.g. hoovers, washing machines, etc.

As puppies become more active, congenital defects not previously apparent may start to show e.g. heart conditions.

Between 8-10 weeks, puppies go through a "fear period" so

traumatic experiences should be avoided during this time. 8-12 weeks is the optimum time for learning.

General Condition

By three weeks puppies can bark! Between three and four weeks puppies can begin to wag their tail!

Temperature

Puppies continue to have increasing control of their body temperature. This should normally be about 37.7°C (100°F) by four weeks of age.

Sight

The vision continues to improve as the puppy has increasing ability to focus. Full vision is probably not attained for several months. The colour of the iris of the eye starts to change by 4-6 weeks of age.

Hearing

This is very acute by three weeks and puppies increasingly learn the relevance of different sounds. Congenital deafness is usually apparent by about 6 weeks of age, observant owners will notice it much earlier from 3 weeks of age. Every puppy of those breeds predisposed to deafness should have their hearing tested at this age.

Mobility

The puppies become increasingly active and start playing simple games within the litter between 3-4 weeks.

Digestion

By 3-4 weeks puppies start to squat to excrete. Reflex elimination ceases by about 4 weeks.

There is considerable variation between different breeds when teeth start erupting. Average ages for first teeth to erupt are:-

Canines:
3-4 weeks

Incisors:
1st - 3-5 weeks
2nd - 3-5 weeks
3rd - 5-6 weeks

Pre-molars:
1st - None in first set of teeth
2nd - 4-6 weeks
3rd - 4-6 weeks
4th - 6-8 weeks

Molars:
None in first set of teeth

CHAPTER TWO

GENERAL CARE OF NEONATAL PUPPIES

CONTENTS

page no.

Priorities in caring for puppies:

GENERAL CARE OF NEONATAL PUPPIES

Puppies are born in a very care dependent state. They can only survive if they receive care which enables them to adapt to extra uterine life. The protected environment of the uterus ensures the puppy is kept at a constant temperature, with the placenta providing a continuous supply of oxygen and nutrients.

The birth process is traumatic especially if it is protracted or if the umbilical cord becomes obstructed, since this effectively cuts off the puppy's supply of oxygen.

In a new born puppy the various systems of its body are immature, e.g. the kidneys are inefficient at conserving water or excreting excess fluid and the liver at detoxifying drugs.

The function of each separate system affects the others, for example if a puppy cries with hunger, this will affect the heart rate, respiration rate, blood oxygen concentration, etc. resulting in stress for the puppy, which will rapidly lead to exhaustion.

To enable the puppy to conserve its precious energy for normal rapid growth, it is important to keep the stresses on the puppy to a minimum by providing the most appropriate care. Some strong sturdy puppies live despite the poor care they receive, but many puppies are more demanding in their requirements. Many potentially healthy puppies die needlessly due to unsuitable management. The requirements of weak or sick puppies are frequently very exacting if the puppies are to survive.

Priorities in Caring for Puppies

Accommodation

A puppy should be nursed in a warm, clean box. A plastic stack-a-box is ideal as it is easy to keep clean; we use Formula-H. The bedding should be both soft and absorbent, such as towelling, and it must be changed regularly. The puppy must always be kept clean and dry. If absorbent paper is put at one end of the box a puppy will usually learn to use it after the first week as a toilet area. Some puppies will do this before their eyes are open.

The puppy will be more restful if it has something to nestle up to, such as a washable soft toy. Puppies are best nursed separately as they tend to suck each other. This sucking can lead to skin trauma. Secondary bacterial infection of the damaged skin often results which may lead to a generalised bacterial infection.

Temperature Control

A thermometer securely fixed to the inside of a box will help to check that the puppies are nursed in the correct temperature. The heat can be provided by a thermostatically controlled heating pad. If a hot water bottle is used it must be carefully padded and extra care must be taken to keep the temperature constant. Infrared lamps are not used at the Clinic. The puppies should be kept at:-

30°C (86°F)for the first two weeks of life
26.5°C (80°F) for the third week
22°-24°C (70°-75°F) for the fourth week
22°C (70°F) from the fifth week onwards.

Identification of Puppies

If you are hand rearing puppies that look very similar, it is important to be able to tell them apart.

Different coloured nail varnish can be painted on the claws. Paint a different paw for each separate puppy. With a large litter different colours can be used.

Example:

Puppy "1" dog - blue front left paw
Puppy "2" dog - blue front right paw
Puppy "3" bitch - pink front left paw etc.

AVERAGE BODY TEMPERATURE

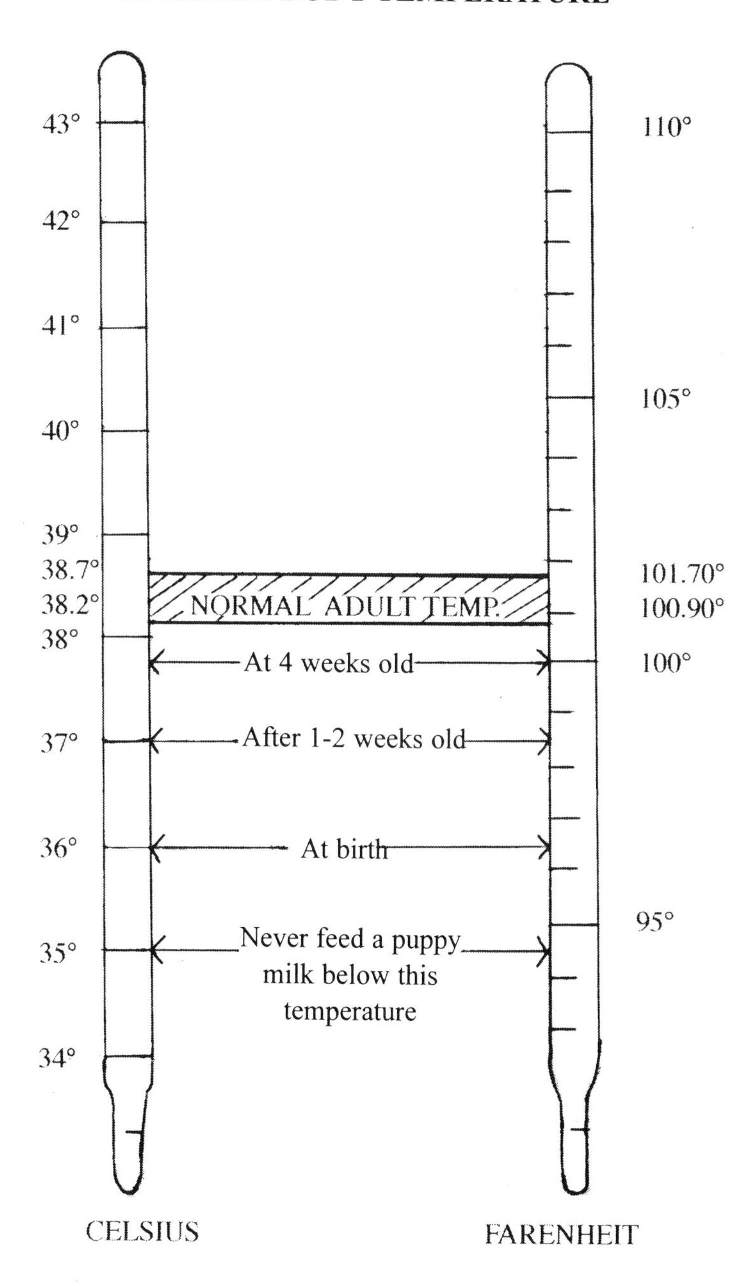

Assessment

The condition of every puppy should be assessed before it is hand reared. This helps to plan the most suitable care for the puppy including its feeding regime, and any specific care the puppy needs. If specialist nursing care or veterinary care is necessary this should be sought as soon as possible.

Regular assessment is essential as the condition of a puppy can deteriorate quickly. Delay in recognising a potential problem and treating it appropriately frequently denies a puppy any chance of survival.

Records

Accurate records of the condition of the puppy and the care a puppy receives can be invaluable both to help the specific puppy and other puppies in the future. These should include details of the whelping, assessment details and feeding and weight charts.

Prevention of Infection

It is important to disinfect your hands before and after handling puppies to prevent cross infection. Hibiscrub can be used as a liquid soap or Hibisol can be applied to clean dry hands. Both are available from chemists.

The plastic box in which the puppy is nursed should be washed carefully each day or as necessary. The puppy should not be returned to the box until it is dry. It is helpful to have a spare box to use whilst the first is being cleaned.

Many disinfectants are unsuitable for use where puppies are being nursed. Some can be lethal. The fumes from pine disinfectants have been known to affect puppies. "FORMULA H" or similar (from pet shops) should be used, but follow the instructions carefully.

NOTE: Puppies that have not received colostrum from their dam are more susceptible to infections. Colostrum is the thick, creamy yellow milk at the start of lactation. This contains more protein and less lactose than normal milk and it is rich in vitamins A and D. It contains antibodies to help protect puppies against infections including many of the canine diseases which the dam has been vaccinated against.

The quantity of colostrum decreases over the first 2/3 days of the lactation.

Absorption of the antibodies occurs in the small intestine of the puppy. Maximum absorption occurs within the first 8 hours. The ability of the puppy to absorb antibodies this way ceases when it is about 24 hours old.

Transportation of Puppies

A small plastic stack-a-box is ideal for the transport of puppies. Alternatively a small cardboard box can be used. The heat source is invariably a hot water bottle. The temperature must be carefully checked before the start of the journey. If this is a long journey a thermos flask of hot water is useful to replenish the content of the bottle when needed.

The temperature in the car must not be allowed to become too hot or too cold. Care must be taken to avoid any "down-draughts" from windows etc. A light towel placed over the box helps to conserve heat.

The longer the journey, the greater is the risk that the puppies will become dehydrated. If the journey is more than 1-2 hours feed the puppies (if possible) before starting the journey with glucose and water. See page 67 for mixture.

CHAPTER THREE

ASSESSING THE HEALTH OF NEONATAL PUPPIES

CONTENTS

ASSESSING THE HEALTH OF NEONATAL PUPPIES

Before any puppy is hand reared the health and hydration status of the puppy should be assessed and it must be checked for obvious congenital deformities e.g. palate defects.

Equipment required:-

A DIGITAL THERMOMETER with a small end bulb.
VASELINE to lubricate the thermometer - preferably K Y Jelly.
ACCURATE SCALES:
Digital Electronic scales are the most accurate. Diet Scales or Letter Scales also give accurate readings.
WARM DAMP WHITE COTTON WOOL PADS
PEN TORCH
STETHOSCOPE - if you have experience using one.

Method of Assessment

All details must be recorded accurately.
Record the dam's history:-

- Age
- The number of previous pregnancies and details of these.
- Details of this pregnancy including any illness and drugs administered during the previous three months.
- Details of this whelping and the health of the bitch and her condition since parturition.

Record the history of each puppy:-

- Specific details since its birth.
- The condition of the puppy since its birth.
- The condition of any siblings since their birth.
- Examine the puppy fully to determine the condition of the puppy including any abnormal signs and symptoms.

Assess your findings and then plan the puppy's care.

NOTE: The puppy should be examined where it can be kept warm.

Examination:

Assess the general condition of the puppy.

- Is the puppy behaving normally or is it behaving strangely?
- Is it limp or restless?
- Is the puppy crying? If so what type of cry is it?
- Check any vomit etc., or diarrhoea and urine output.

Hydration Status - "skin pinch test"

Gently pinch the skin over the shoulders on the side of the puppy's neck. This is more accurate in newborn puppies than pinching at the base of the neck. If the puppy is dehydrated the skin stays up in a peak for a time when you let go.

Temperature

Insert a well lubricated thermometer just inside the rectum. Be very gentle as the delicate tissues of a tiny puppy are easily damaged. NEVER USE A THERMOMETER WITH A LARGE BULB

Weight

Weigh the puppy. Compare this with:

i) The average expected weight for a puppy of the same age and breed, that has been reared by its dam.
ii) Any previous weights recorded for this particular puppy.

Check the **heart rate** by placing the little finger behind the puppy's left elbow. This is normally 200 beats per minute. This can be difficult to feel so a stethoscope can be helpful.

Check the **respiratory rate**. A stethoscope is useful to listen for any respiratory problems, but if you hold the puppy up to your ear you may hear wheezing or rattling of the chest.

Head and Skull

Check the size and shape of the head.

Check for persistent fontanelle by placing the pad of your little finger on the midline of the forehead between the eyes. Gently stroke backwards towards the top of the skull. Feel for an opening between the two fontanelle bones where the frontal bones have not fused.

Eyes

Check for the presence of the eyes, their size and position.

Ears

Check these for size and position.

Nose

Check the nostrils are clear. Look for any signs of mucus, pus, blood, milk, etc.

Mouth

Note the colour of the tongue and gums. These should be a warm pink, not red. Use a pen torch to check the mouth is free of any obstruction such as bedding or hair that could make nursing difficult. Also check the roof the mouth for any sign of a cleft palate or a split in the hard palate. Small holes can be very hard to detect.

Place a clean finger in the mouth and feel if the suck reflex is present. Is the mouth moist? It should be warm to touch.

Rib Cage

Check this is symmetrical with no obvious signs of fractures. Is the chest flattened - so the puppy looks as though it has been under a steam roller? Check if the sternum is protruding into the chest.

Limbs

Check each of the limbs in turn to check that they are in the normal position and without deformity. In toy breeds check in particular for luxation of the patella. Check all the toes are present. Make a note of back dew claws which may have to be removed. Is there any sign of injury? Note any signs of paralysis or tendon contractures.

Check the muscle tone. Decreased tone is often an early sign of illness in a puppy.

Look at the pads of the feet - are they rounded or have they become flattened? (If this is the case puppy may be de-hydrated.) If they are not pigmented black, note the colour. Squeeze the membranes between the pads on the feet to check for pain perception. Sore pads can be caused by unsuitable bedding.

Abdomen

Note the colour of the skin.

Check the umbilicus for inflammation, infection including signs of pus, swelling or if it is leaking urine.

Check the size of the abdomen and if it feels hard or soft. The abdomen is normally enlarged after nursing. Is there any sign of abnormality of the abdominal wall?

Check the external genitalia for any sign of inflammation e.g. urine burn, damage from siblings sucking etc. Stimulate micturition by stroking the abdomen with warm, damp, white cotton wool. Urine should not be coloured. Check the anus is present and working! Note the colour, consistency and quantity of motion passed. Is the anus sore or is there any sign of prolapse.

The Spine and Tail

Check for any abnormality e.g. Spina Bifida, kinky tail or any injury, or absent tail. This usually indicates an internal abnormality.

Skin and Coat

Check for complete hair cover especially around the hocks, stifles and around the muzzle. Can be a useful guide for assessing maturity.

Check for wounds from an over zealous mother or siblings sucking etc.

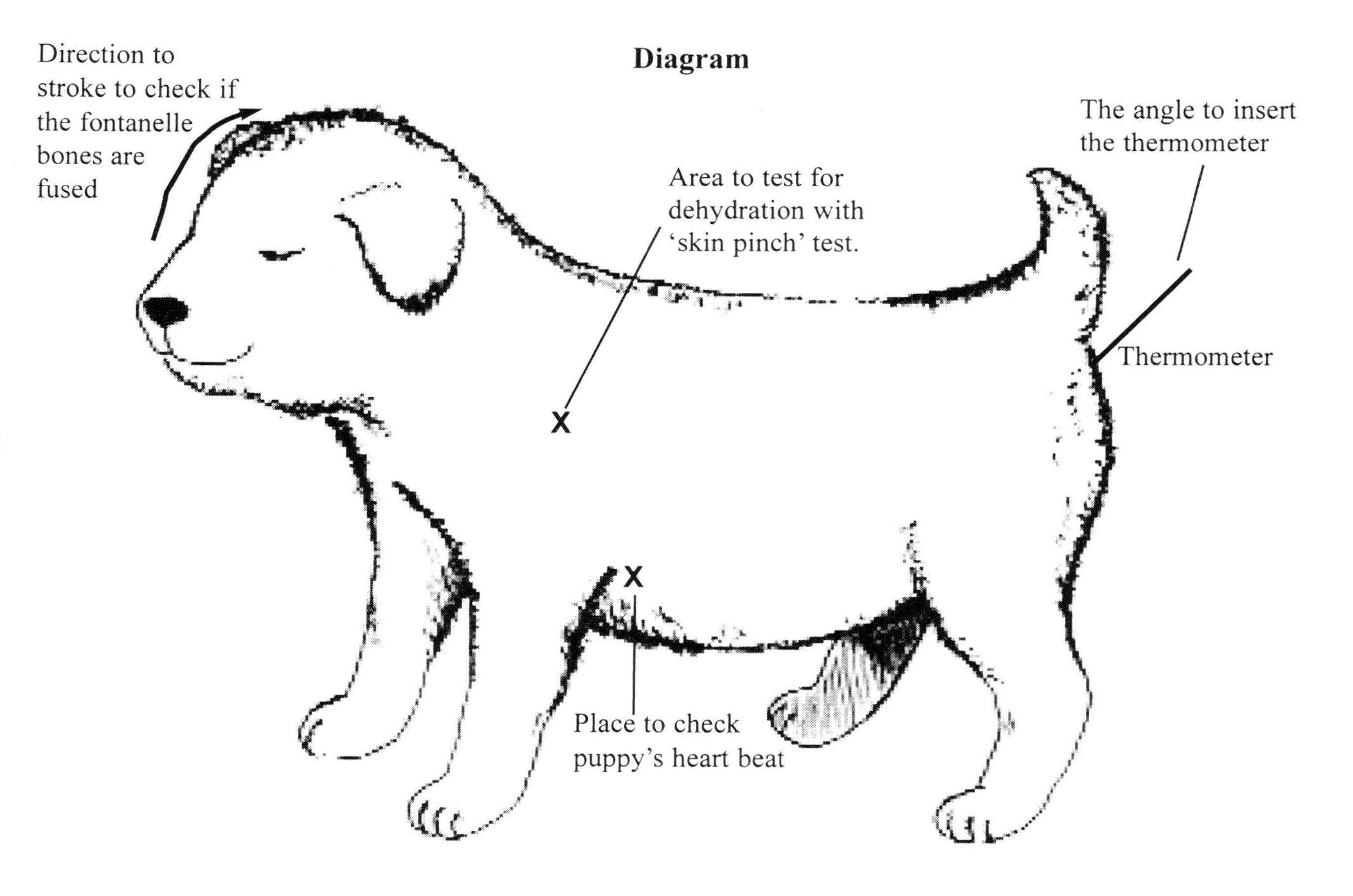
Diagram
Direction to stroke to check if the fontanelle bones are fused
Area to test for dehydration with 'skin pinch' test.
The angle to insert the thermometer
Thermometer
Place to check puppy's heart beat

ASSESSMENT CHART

DOB - Time ______________ Length of gestation _____________

Temperature ______________ Weight _______________________

Has the puppy received colostrum_____________

General Condition

Hydration status ___________ Has the puppy vomited __________

Is the puppy restless ________ Is the puppy crying _____________

Is the puppy limp ___________ Type of cry ___________________

Head and Skull

Shape ___________________

Size _____________________

Open fontanelle ___________

Signs of injury ____

Ears: Position _____________ Nose: Patancy _______________

Size _______________ Discharge:_____________

Milk _________________

Pus __________________

Mucus ______________

Blood ________________

Eyes: Presence ___________________

Position ___________________

Condition __________________ i.e. swollen eye lids

Mouth: Colour of mucus membranes ____________________

Are mucus membranes moist ____________________

Suck reflex ____________________

Temperature to touch ____________________

Incomplete soft palate ____________________

Cleft Palate ____________________

Rib Cage

Shape of Rib Cage ____________________

Symmetrical ____________ Flat Chest ____________

Funnel Chest ____________ Other abnormality ____________

Respiratory rate ________ /minute. Character________

Pulse rate __________ /minute. Rhythm __________

Character ________

Limbs

Presence of limbs ________ Any sign of injury __________

Position of limbs _________ Colour of pads ____________

Presence of toes __________

Abdomen

Colour of skin______________ Is it hard? Yes/No

Is it enlarged Yes/No Is it soft? Yes/No

Any abnormality of abdominal wall ____________________

Umbilicus: Any sign of infection ____________________

Any sign of injury ____________________

(N.B. Normally the cord drops off at 2-3 days)

Stimulate micturition:

Colour ____________________________

Quantity ___________________________

Other features? e.g. Haematuria ____________________ (Blood in urine)

Stimulate defecation:

Patancy of anus? Yes/No

State of anus e.g. sore ____________________

Evidence of constipation __________________

Colour/texture of stool ____________________

Diarrhoea?   Yes/No

Spine and Tail

Any deformity __________________________

Skin

Is there hair cover, especially around muzzle and paws? __________

Condition of coat ________________________

Presence of debris________________________

Presence of wounds_______________________

Skin infections ____________________________

CHAPTER FOUR

REVIEWING THE ASSESSMENT

CONTENTS

REVIEWING THE ASSESSMENT

The most helpful findings when reviewing a puppy's health care are the puppy's temperature, hydration status and the colour of the mucus membranes. Puppies frequently have more than one problem, so it is important to determine which should receive priority. It is important to try to achieve normothermia, correct the hydration status and then treat any other condition as necessary.

Temperature

A neonatal puppy should have a temperature that is lower than adult dogs. At birth the average puppy's temperature is 36°C (96.8°F) rising to 37°C (98.6°F) after one to two weeks. By four weeks it should have risen to just under 38°C (100°F).

Hypothermia - Sub-normal temperature below 35°C refer to page 38.

A puppy's temperature falls if its environment is too cold. The temperature must be raised to enable all the systems of the body to function effectively. NEVER FEED A PUPPY MILK IF ITS TEMPERATURE IS LESS THAN 35°C (95°F). Digestion can not occur at temperatures below 34.4°C (94°F). TREATMENT IS URGENT.

Causes include:

Being nursed in too cold an environment
Hypoglycaemia and malnutrition
Shock
Fading puppy syndrome
Hydrocephalus (fluid on the brain - open fontanelle)

Hyperthermia - (Heat Stroke) refer to page 39.

This is caused by a puppy being nursed in an overheated environment. It is important to correct this. After one hour re-check the puppy's rectal temperature to see if it is returning to normal. It should have recovered within 4-5 hours.

Pyrexia - (raised body temperature)

If, despite being nursed at the correct environmental temperature, a puppy has a raised temperature, this normally indicates the presence of infection. These may include septicaemia, pneumonia or infected wounds.

Hydration Status

Dehydration can be detected by the "skin pinch test". The pads of the feet appear flat. The mouth will feel dry. Any urine passed will be strong and dark yellow in colour (urine is normally colourless), motions hard and lumpy possibly none at all - constipated. The temperature is usually normal or sub-normal. TREATMENT IS URGENT.

Colour of the Mucous Membranes

Assessment is based on the colour of the mouth and tongue, the abdomen and the paws. The colour of these give an indication of the problem:

Deep Cherry Red frequently indicates a bacterial infection. Look for signs of systemic infection e.g. septicaemia or localised infection e.g. pneumonia.

Bright Red occurs with hyperthermia.

Pale membranes often indicate hypothermia or poor circulation or anaemia, or the early stages of reduced oxygen supply to the tissues leading to collapse and low body temperature.

Grey/Blue Colour indicates cyanosis (respiratory dysfunction) resulting from lack of oxygen in the puppy's blood.

Mauve or Dark Blue occurs with circulatory/respiratory failure and collapse, which frequently causes severe permanent damage to the main organs of the body, including the brain. These puppies usually die. Causes include terminal hypothermia, hyperthermia.

Respiratory Problems

Breathing should appear regular in both depth and rate. Shortness of breath and cyanosis (blueness) are not usually obvious until a puppy is seriously ill.

A flat chested puppy will also have severe breathing difficulties.

Nasal Discharges

These can indicate a number of problems:

- Pus is a sign of infection in the nasal passages secondary to accumulation of milk or food.
- Look for signs of holes or a split in the palate.
- Blood is often caused by injury or bleeding from the lungs or due to immature lungs.

Very Small Puppies

To be able to assess the significance of the problem it is important to know the average birth weight and normal growth rate for puppies of the specific breed concerned. Common causes include:

- Pre-Term/Immaturity
- Congenital problems especially cardio-respiratory problems.
- Unsatisfactory conditions *in utero*.

Euthanasia

Whenever it becomes apparent that a puppy has little chance of leading a normal active life, it should be spared further suffering and euthanased. Some genetic defects do not prevent a dog leading a full, happy life but the puppy must be neutered to ensure they cannot be bred from thus not passing on the fault to their offspring.

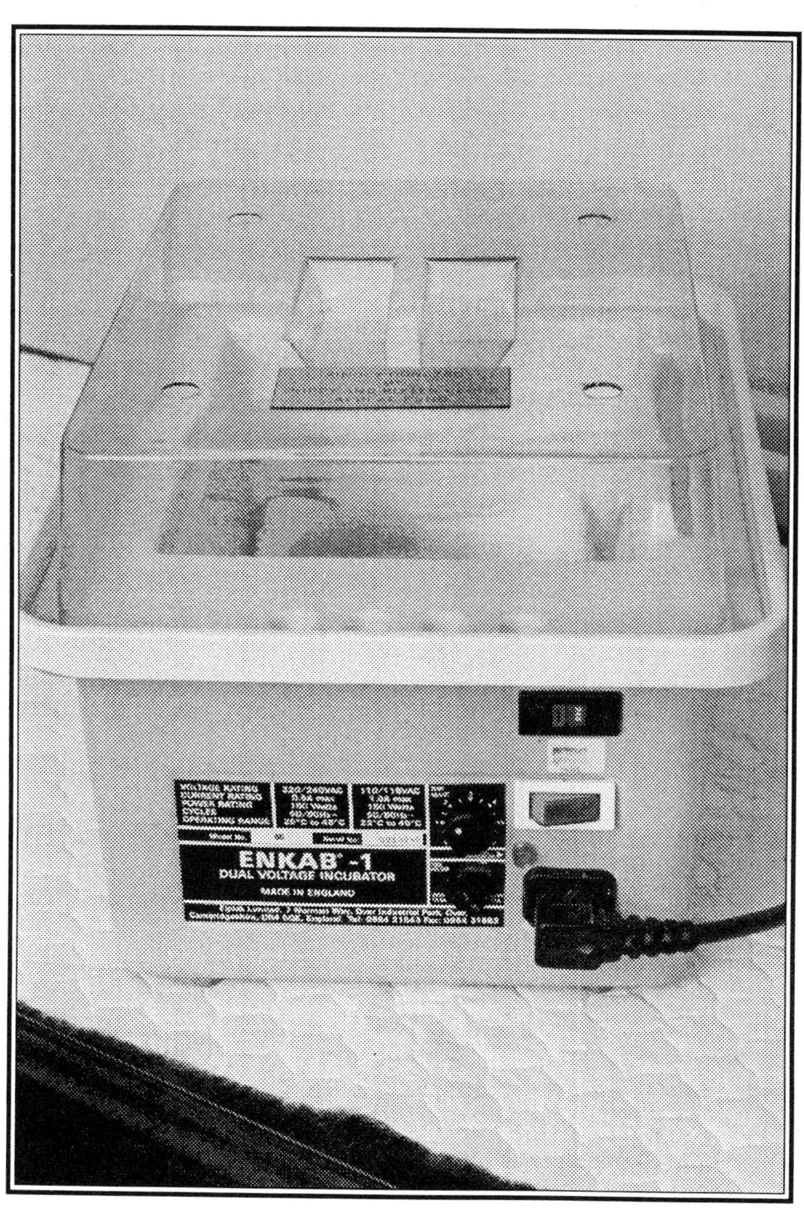

Small incubator for a very small puppy - a pre-term puppy may spend up to 7 days in this environment

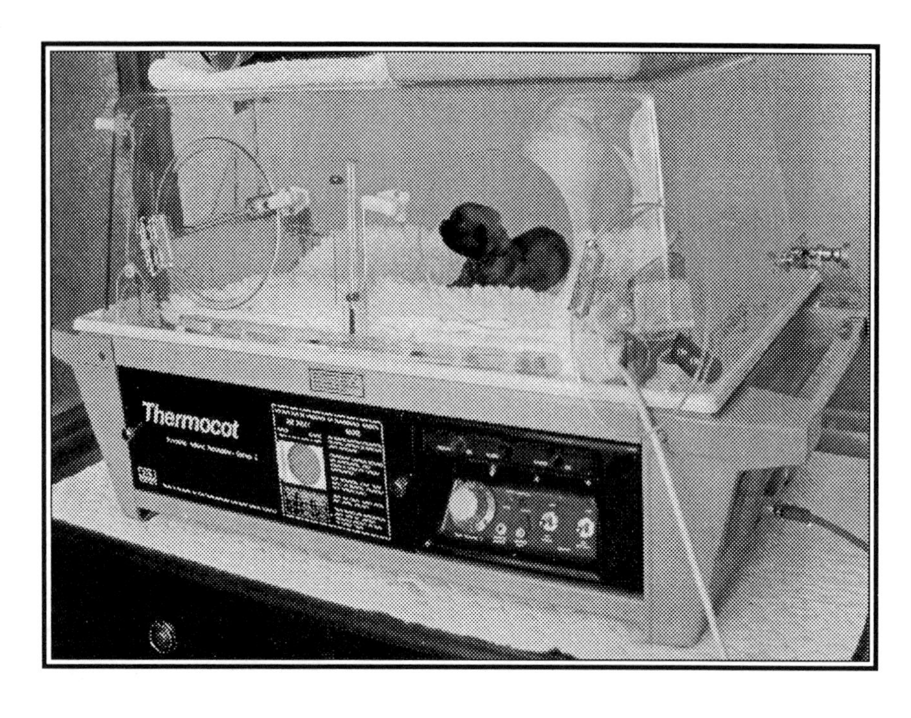

Portable incubator used for large puppies - used for assesment of new arrivals to the clinic.

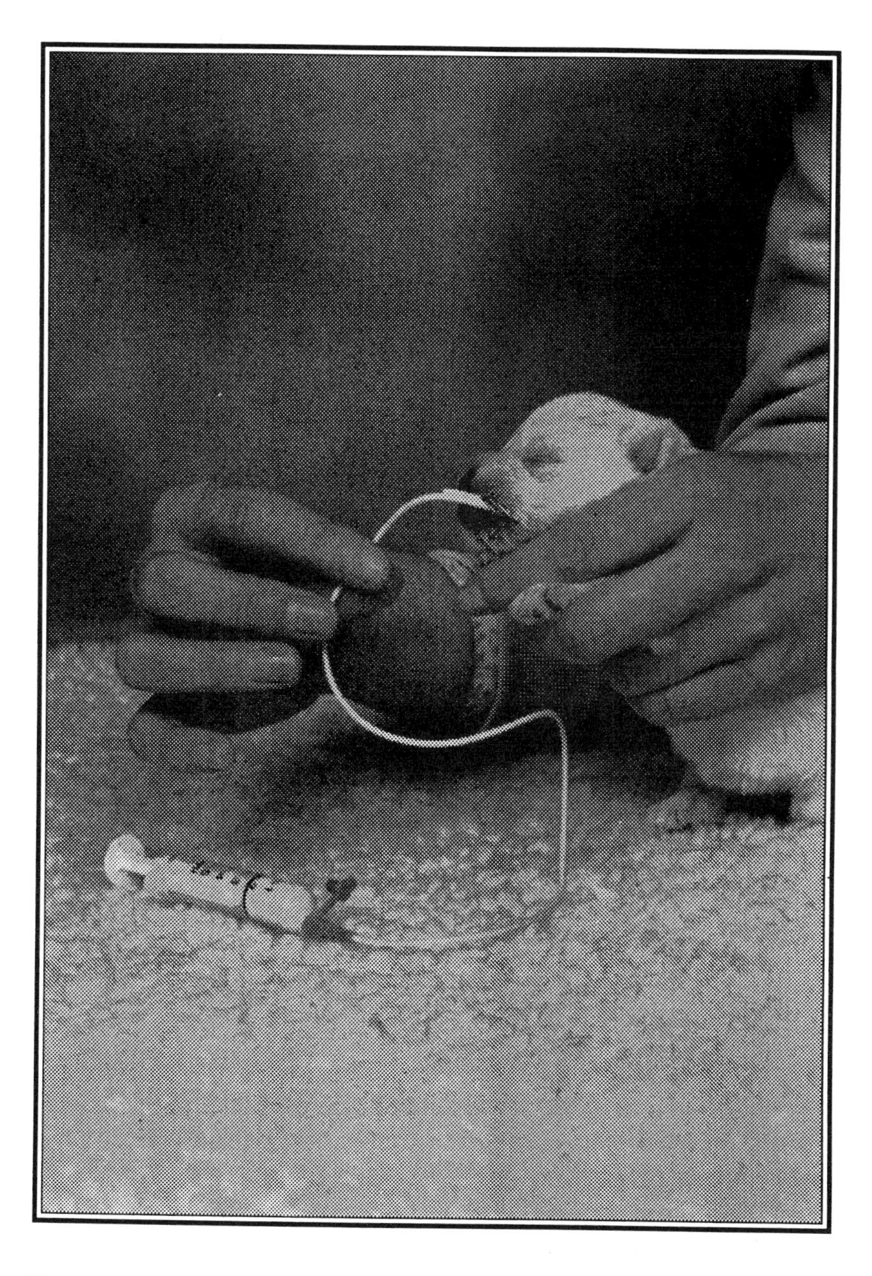

Gastric tube feeding measured for length externally by tape marker

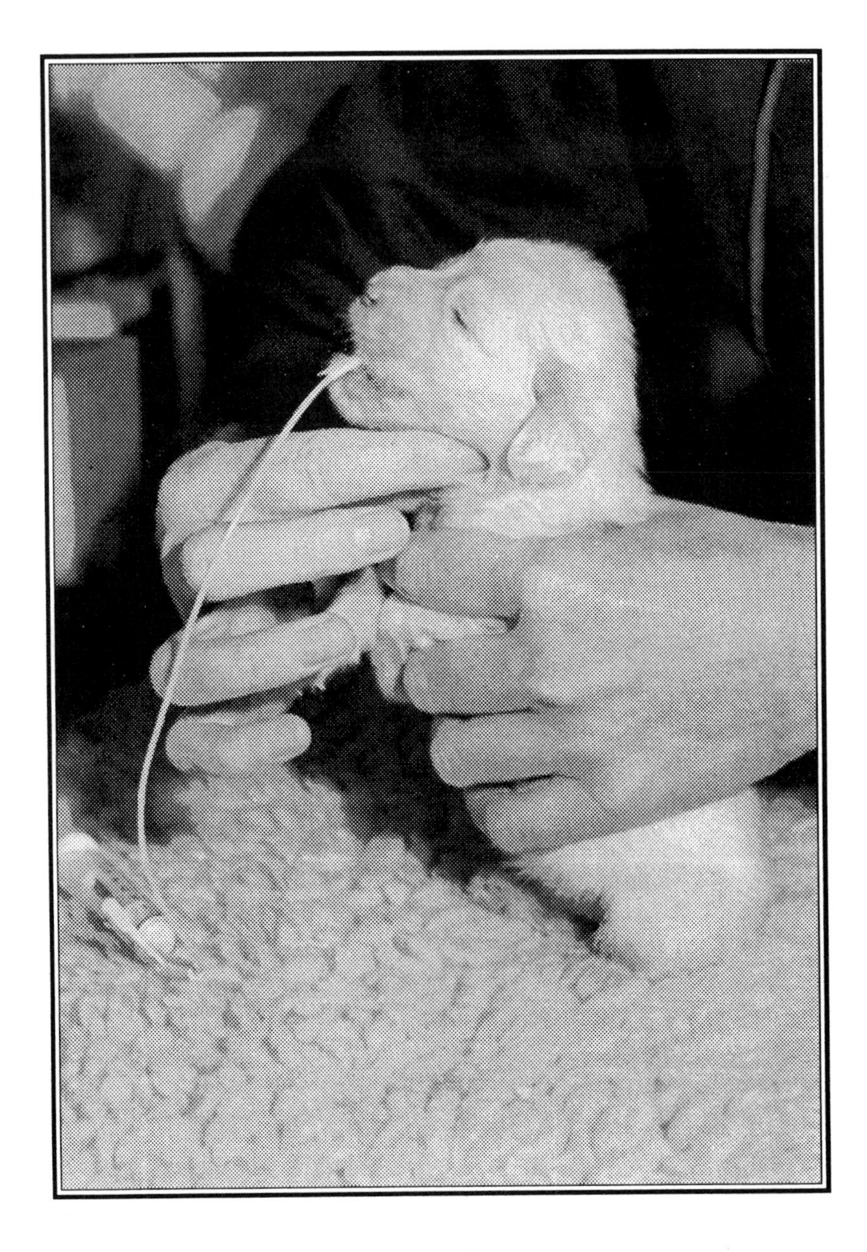

Gastric tube feeding. Showing tube inserted and checking for correct position before milk is administered.

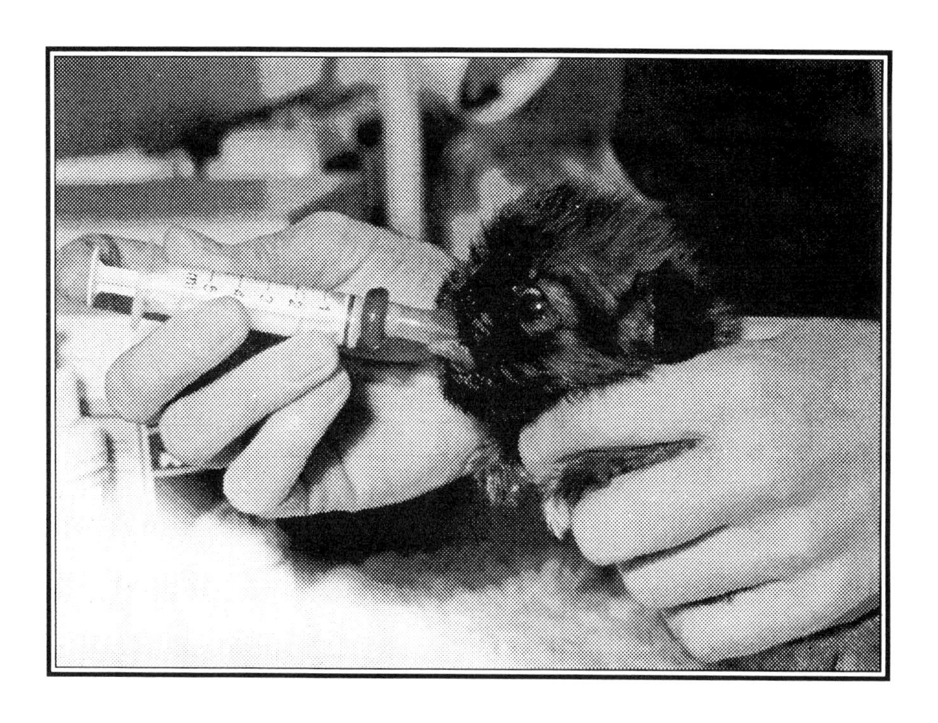

Typical Puppy being fed from syringe via teat prior to weaning onto solids.

Puppy weaned on 'Hills' Canine Growth - made into small round balls rolled by hand according to size of puppy.

CHAPTER FIVE

CLINICAL CONDITIONS

CONTENTS

The condition of every puppy will be different. Treatment notes can only be a guide based on our personal experience at the Clinic. Please adapt the suggestions given according to the condition of each individual puppy in consultation with your vetinary surgeon.

Pre-term Puppies

In the Clinics experience we have noted that many breeds whelp two or three days early, without any problems occurring. There is however a variation between breeds in normal gestation time but when puppies are born five or more days earlier than their breed average, their ability to survive diminishes rapidly.

Signs

These puppies are frequently small, with incomplete hair around the muzzle, hocks and stifles.

They may have a deficiency of a substance called surfactant, which normally lines the lungs and therefore allows normal breathing. Lack of surfactant can result in the lungs collapsing after each breath. This is a tremendous strain on the puppy and very often fatal.

Treatment

It is of paramount importance that the dam's colostrum is fed to the puppies in the first few hours of life whenever possible. Net-Tex Agricultural market a product which is an alternative to bitches colostrum. Great care should be taken to prevent stress to these puppies. Give glucose solution for the first feed, then feed the puppy diluted milk or colostrum solution.

By waiting until the expected date of birth of the puppy before feeding full strength milk, the strain on the immature digestive system is reduced. Very premature puppies that are unable to suck adequately for their needs require specialist nursing.

Specialist Care

Puppies born more than a few days early should be tube fed.

Steroids together with antibodies can be administered by a veterinary surgeon, to help immature lungs.

Hypothermia

Puppies get cold quickly as they have no control over their body temperature when they are born. This is a very frequent cause of neonatal death.

Signs

These puppies feel cold and limp and blood pressure drops. As their temperature drops their circulation slows down and the paws, abdomen, tongue and the gums become pale due to the reduced oxygen supply. They will become comatosed unless treated promptly. None of the main organs of the body, including their digestive system, can function normally until the circulation has improved.

These puppies can develop hypoglycemia, as the puppy quickly uses up the small store of glucose in the liver in an attempt to maintain its body temperature, this frequently occurs with Hydrocephalus, Fading Puppy Syndrome, shock etc.

Treatment

The first priority is to raise the puppy's temperature. This must be done SLOWLY to avoid the puppy going into shock and possibly developing heart failure. It may take a couple of hours or more to warm the puppy, depending on how cold it has become. The puppy should be wrapped in a piece of cotton material, little more than the puppy's nose and mouth left uncovered. Place the wrapped puppy in a warm box at 30°C (86°F) on a warm hot water bottle or heated pad.

Take the puppy's temperature regularly and adjust the temperature in the box, so the puppy warms up gradually without becoming over-heated. NEVER feed a puppy milk until the circulation has improved because the digestive system cannot function. Any milk feed given when the rectal temperature is less than 34.4°C (94°F) will stagnate in the stomach adding to the puppy's problems. As the puppy warms up, the colour of the gums will become pink. Feel for a suck reflex, if this is not present the puppy will have to be tube fed with glucose and electrolyte solution.

If sucking reflexes persist start feeding with a small quantity (possibly only ½ml) of glucose solution every 20 to 30 minutes. Hopefully after two or three feeds the puppy will be strong enough for the frequency of feed to be decreased and the amount fed increased. Gradually restart milk feeds. Progress will vary considerably with the individual puppy's condition.

Specialist Nursing

This will be required if the suck reflex does not return when the puppy's temperature rises.

Prognosis

If treatment is started when the colour of the mucous membranes is pale there is a chance of saving the puppy.

If the colour of the membranes are mauve or purple the puppy will have circulatory collapse. This will cause permanent damage to the main organs of the body, and the oxygen supply to the brain will have been reduced. These puppies are likely to die.

Hyperthermia - Heat Stroke

This can occur when a puppy is nursed where it becomes overheated. New-born puppies are at special risk of developing this as they are unable to control their body temperature.

Signs

The severity of the signs depend on the degree of overheating. The body temperature will be raised and the mucous membranes of the mouth become bright red. Gradually as the breathing becomes laboured the puppy will become cyanosed and go into shock. Fits/convulsions, may occur.

Treatment

Aim to reduce the temperature to about 37.7°C (100°F) within ten minutes, by removing the puppy from the heat source and gently massaging the puppy with an ice-cube in a plastic bag. Try to keep the puppy dry. Take care not to induce hypothermia but it is important to discover and rectify the reason for the hyperthermia. It is often caused by a puppy being nursed on an over-hot, hot water bottle, on a heating pad with faulty thermostat or under too hot an infra red lamp.

Specialist Nursing

This will be required if the puppy develops shock. Delayed complications such as renal kidney failure will need specialist care.

Dehydration

This occurs when a puppy has insufficient fluid intake for the body to function normally or has excessive fluid loss e.g. diarrhoea or vomiting. This can occur because a puppy is unable to suck adequately for its need (hypoglycoemia is often a first sign).

Signs

The skin remains raised following the "skin pinch test". The urine becomes dark in colour because it is concentrated. It may not be possible to stimulate the puppy to urinate. The motions become hard and lumpy, and the puppy will become constipated.

Other signs include: the mouth feels dry to the touch and the paws appear to have flat pads (not rounded as normal).

Treatment

These puppies should be given glucose and electrolyte solution to rehydrate them. To prevent overstraining the puppy's system it should be given little and often. At first, give 1 - 1½ ml depending on the size of the puppy, every half hour. When the puppy's condition improves gradually increase the amount you feed as you reduce the frequency of the feeds. Milk should be re-introduced gradually. Severe dehydration will need parenteral (by injection) fluids administered by a veterinary surgeon.

Specialist Nursing

Weak puppies should be fed by gastric tube. If the puppy is constipated it should be given an enema by a veterinary surgeon or specialist nurse.

Special Note

It is important to discover and remedy the cause of this occurring. Problems with the maternal milk supply usually causes problems with the smallest, weakest puppy first. Gradually the rest of the litter will become affected until the cause of the situation is found and appropriate measures taken. Some common maternal causes are:-

i) Inadequate milk supply. Since the dam's milk is produced largely on a supply and demand basis, carefully massaging the mammary area can stimulate the milk supply. Always ensure the dam has an adequate fluid intake. Light exercise also stimulates the production of milk.

ii) Congestion of one or more of the milk glands - these should receive prompt treatment to prevent mastitis developing. Matted long hair can prevent the nipples being used. Carefully massage the enlarged gland with a breast cream) available from a pharmacy, then gently withdraw some of the milk. When the milk is flowing freely a strong puppy should be placed on the teat to empty the gland. Keep a careful watch on the mammary area for the first few days after whelping until the supply matches the demand. Mastitis will require treatment by the veterinary surgeon, normally with an antibiotic. If a puppy is allowed to suck from an infected mammary gland, the puppy may develop a gastroenteritis.

iii) Sore nipples occur quickly if puppies nails are not cut short regularly. This can make a bitch very reluctant to allow puppies to suckle. Cut off the sharp ends of the puppies claws and apply breast cream to the dam's mammary area.

iv) After several litters, the teats of the dam can become thickened and enlarged. Small weak puppies may have difficulty sucking from these.

v) Excessive competition in a litter can prevent the weakest puppy suckling adequately - ensure little pups are given a chance.

vi) A restless dam will often prevent the litter from suckling adequately. If in doubt ask your veterinary surgeon to check the bitch for a possible cause.

Hypoglycaemia

Hypoglycaemia is low blood glucose. The most usual cause of this is because a puppy is unable to feed adequately. Small weak puppies are at special risk. Neonatal puppies are only able to store a very limited supply of glucose, so it is important they are not starved for more than a few hours to prevent this condition developing.

First Aid – Net-Tex market a product called Nutri-Drops, which has proved useful as an emergency measure.

Puppies with sepsis need glucose to fight infection, so they must be fed frequently (at least every 2 hours day and night).

Signs

These puppies are frequently dehydrated and hypothermic. They may cry, have respiratory distress and decreased heart rate. As the condition progresses the puppy will go limp and may become comatosed resulting in severe neurological damage, convulsions and probably death.

Treatment

Early treatment is essential. If the puppy is hypothermic the first priority is to raise the puppy's temperature above 35°C (95°F) as described earlier.

The puppy should then be fed ½ - 1ml of glucose and electrolyte solution (depending on the size of the puppy) every half hour. Gradually, the amount fed can be increased and the frequency of feeds reduced. Milk should be re-introduced gradually. Do not overfeed with concentrated glucose solutions as this can cause diarrhoea which can increase dehydration of the puppy

Specialist Care

If the puppy is limp, without a suck reflex the only chance to save the puppy is by intensive nursing care so that it may be fed by tube or given subcutaneous fluids.

Careful temperature regulation in an incubator and tube feeding may save the puppy. Any other condition that contributed to the condition occurring will require appropriate care i.e. lack of nutrition.

Shock

Shock is the name for collapse that results from circulatory failure. The heart is unable to supply all of the tissues in the body with adequate blood to provide enough oxygen for them to function normally. There are many causes including: hypothermia, sudden blood loss from internal bleeding or from the umbilical cord.

Signs

The puppy's blood pressure will drop abruptly. Other signs include general weakness, possible loss of consciousness, a weak rapid irregular heart beat, subnormal temperature, paleness of the tongue and gums, reduced output of urine and shallow breathing.

If the puppy is cold treat it as for hypothermia, otherwise maintain its temperature carefully at 36°- 37°C (97°- 98.6°F). Overheating too quickly will increase the degree of shock.

Treatment

If the puppy is unconscious do not attempt to feed it but seek immediate veterinary help and advice. If the puppy is conscious and its temperature is normal, feed it half hourly with electrolyte solution. Give 1- 1½ ml according to the size of the puppy. As the puppy improves increase the volume you feed as you decrease the frequency of the feeds. Slowly re-introduce milk feeds.

Specialist Care

The puppy is usually so weak that it needs to be tube fed.

Hypoxia - Oxygen Starvation.

Oxygen starvation can result from a prolonged birth, particularly difficult, breech births. This is often the result of placental failure or umbilical cord obstruction during the birth or respiratory obstruction.

Signs

These puppies can appear less active than their litter mates and have a weak or absent suck reflex. The puppies are often too weak to survive in the litter and will quickly become dehydrated if left untreated.

Treatment

It is essential to recognise these puppies quickly after birth and to start treatment promptly.

The puppy should be fed at half hourly intervals with 1 - 1½ ml of glucose solution, according to the size of the puppy. As the puppy's condition improves gradually increase the amount you feed when you reduce the frequency of the feeds. Milk feeds should be introduced gradually before returning the puppy to the litter where it should be accepted by the mother when it has recovered.

Alternatively, with a co-operative dam, express a drop of milk from a teat, then put the puppy on the teat (as with bottle feeding). Hold the puppy in place and stimulate it to suck by stroking either side of the muzzle. This must be repeated little and often dependent on the puppy's condition, until it can manage unaided.

To check if the puppy has fed effectively, it can be test weighed on accurate scales before and after a feed.

Specialist Care

If the suck reflex cannot be stimulated adequately, the puppy will need tube feeding.

Prognosis

These puppies should show definite signs of improvement within 24 hours if they are going to recover.

Cleft Palates

This is the failure of the hard and/or soft palate to fuse during uterine development. Palate problems can range from minute pin-prick holes to a large longitudinal fissure in the roof of the mouth, or even total deficit of both palates. In a few breeds, the condition is thought to be hereditary, caused by a simple recessive trait, but most cases are sporadic and believed to be due to adverse conditions during early foetal development. Primary causes are thought to include metabolic disturbances and also the administration of certain drugs early in the gestation. Irradiation may also cause the problem!!

Signs

These vary according to the severity of the defect. Signs may include poor growth, and presence of milk at the nostrils both during and after feeding. Coughing and sneezing may occur when sucking. These puppies are susceptible to respiratory infection. Aspiration pneumonia and starvation can be fatal if the condition is undetected. Small holes in the palate can easily be missed at birth, as they can be as fine as a pin-prick. When these puppies suck, their feed is forced through the holes in the nasal passages, and you may see bubbles of milk at the nose. These puppies fail to thrive in the litter and the holes cannot heal if the puppy is allowed to suckle.

CLEFT PALATE

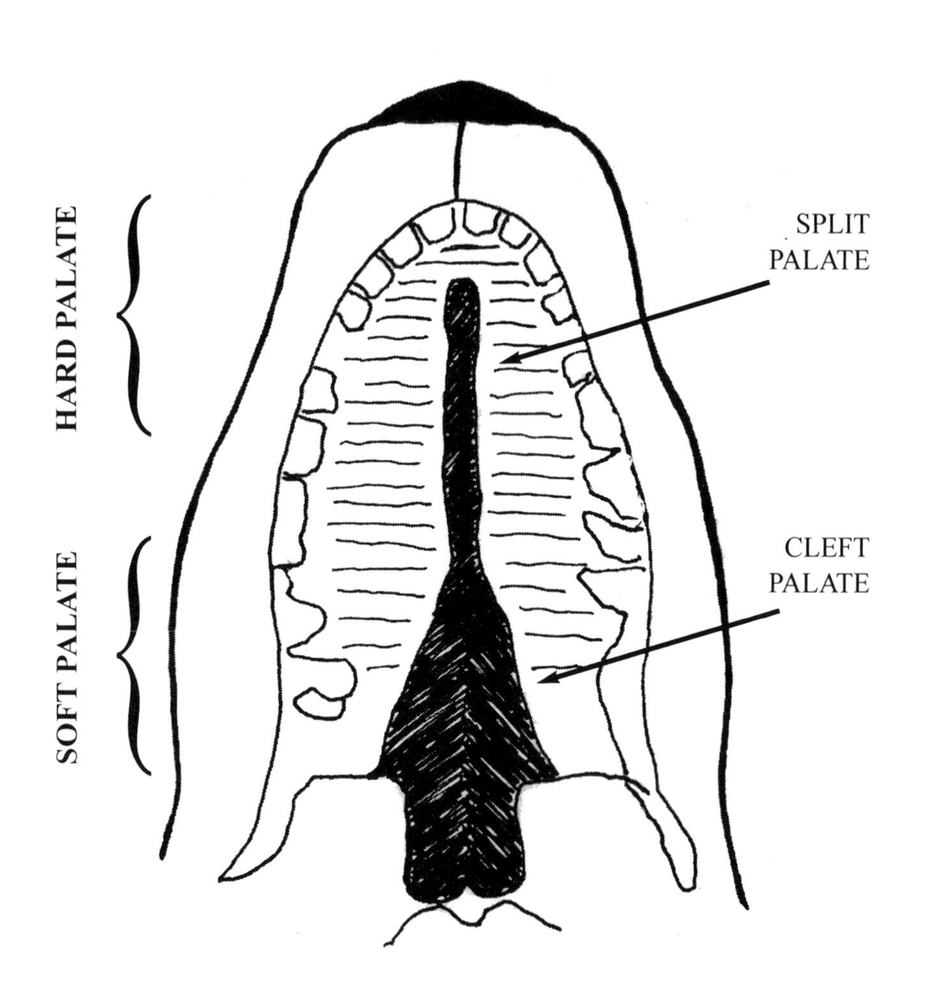

DEFINITION:
FISSURE OR LONGITUDINAL OPENING IN THE ROOF OF THE MOUTH USUALLY DUE TO A CONGENITAL DEFECT. (FAILURE OF THE MEDIAL PLATES OF THE PALATE TO MEET UP.)

Treatment and Specialist Nursing

It is essential these puppies are tube fed adequate nutrition. Fine holes may seal in as few as 4-5 days. Puppies with larger defects can often be successfully reared by tube feeding until the puppy is large enough for surgery to be performed; from 6-8 weeks for the soft palate and approximately 6 months for the repair of the hard palate.

Prognosis

These puppies, after corrective surgery are capable of leading a normal life.

However, in view of the problems rearing these puppies, most owners opt for euthanasia. All animals with cleft repaired palates should be neutered (see page 28).

Pneumonia

This is an inflammatory condition of the lungs. There are various types including:

i) Aspiration caused by a puppy inhaling a substance which irritates the lungs such as milk. It is frequently caused by attempts to feed a puppy by dropping milk onto its tongue with a dropper or syringe. Bottle feeding with a teat is much safer if the puppy is able to suck.

ii) Bacterial and viral infections can cause pneumonia.

iii) Verminous pneumonia can occasionally occur following the migration of Toxacara larvae (roundworm larvae) to the lungs.

Signs

These vary both with the cause of the pneumonia and the severity of the condition. There is usually a very rapid onset of signs with aspiration pneumonia.

The puppies develop fever with irregular, laboured breathing. They will refuse food. If the puppy has the strength it makes a sick puppy cry (like a seagull).

Gradually you will hear a rattling noise in the chest as the lungs become congested and the puppy may start to gasp. The puppy will gradually become limp and cyanosed from lack of oxygen.

Specialist Care

These puppies are usually too sick to be nursed at home. This will include tube feeding and antibiotics. Oxygen is often helpful.

Special Note

If a puppy inhales milk - hold the puppy firmly, and shake it sharply downwards supporting its neck when clearing the lungs after birth. Prompt clearing of the lungs can help prevent aspiration pneumonia developing. The cough reflex is usually present when the puppy is two weeks old.

Pectus Excavatum - Funnel Chest

In this condition the sternum presses into the thorax. The rib cage will be flattened in appearance and the sternum may collapse inwards as the puppy breathes.

Signs

The symptoms vary considerably according to the severity of the deformity. If the condition is mild the puppy may thrive in the nest and the deformity may only be found on palpitation of the chest wall. In serious cases the reduced lung capacity results in poor growth rate, breathing difficulties and reduced exercise tolerance. In severe cases the puppy will be unable to suck adequately for its needs and show signs of dehydration and debilitation.

Treatment

If the condition is not severe, the puppy can be reared by the dam successfully.

NORMAL RIB CAGE

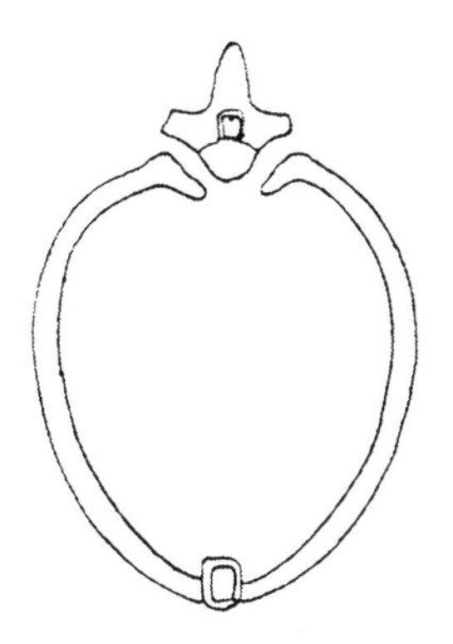

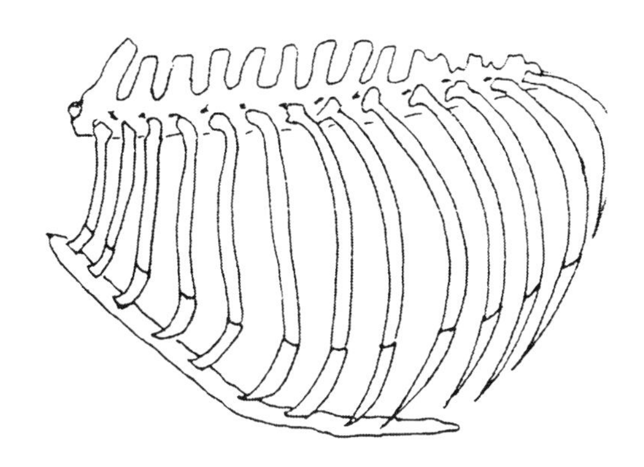

FLAT CHEST

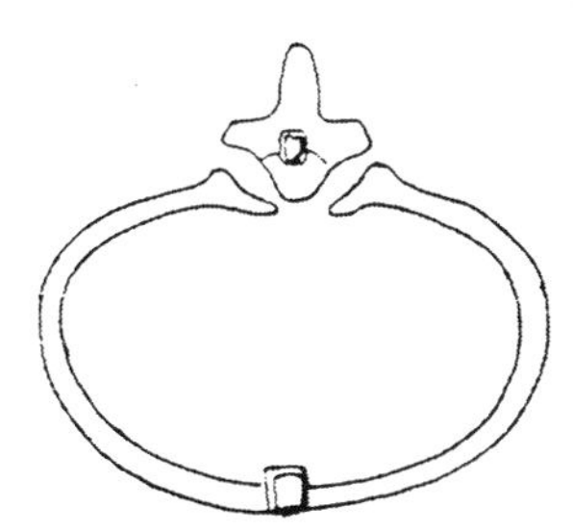

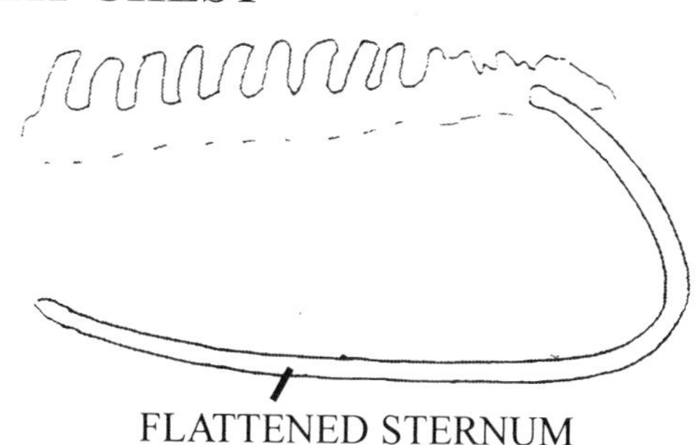

PECTUS EXCAVATUM (FUNNEL CHEST)

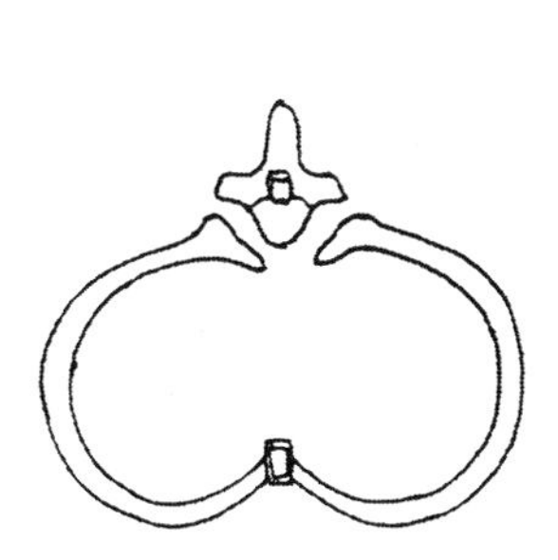

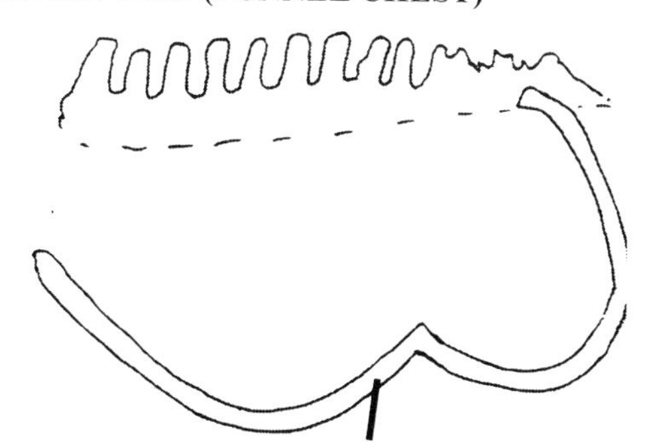

Specialist Care

X-rays can be used to assess the degree of deformity. Tube feeding will be necessary for severe cases. At the clinic, we have found the deformity may correct itself as the puppy grows. Care is taken to encourage the puppy to sleep on its side, or on its back to relieve the pressure on the chest. Resting the puppy's head on a suitable soft toy will also help the puppy's breathing.

Special Note

Current research is indicating there may be a hereditary implication in some breeds but often the condition occurs sporadically.

Flat Puppy Syndrome - Swimmer Puppies

These puppies have similar chest deformity as with funnel chest but there is no curvature of the sternum, just flattening of the thorax. It is frequently associated with an inability of the puppy to stand. It can occur in any breed but tends to be most common in the broad, heavy, short legged breeds such as Scottish Terriers.

Signs

At about 10 days puppies normally come up first on their front legs raising their chest off the ground, and then a few days later on their back legs raising their rear off the ground. Swimmer puppies fail to do this, and as they grow their rapid weight gain often makes standing impossible. Puppies most at risk seem to be the very weak puppies due to muscle wastage, or the very big, heavy puppies. The puppies take the look of a frog with front and rear legs splayed sideways. This throws considerable strain on the thorax encouraging the flat chest deformity and can result in respiratory distress.

Treatment

Various methods have been devised to encourage the puppy to stand on its legs and to strengthen the leg muscles to enable the puppy to walk. As soon as the condition is noticed the puppy should be nursed on a soft surface to minimise the flattening of the chest e.g. polyester fur blanket over a layer of foam. Flat chests can frequently be corrected if the condition is noticed and managed early. Whenever the puppy wakes, place a hand under the puppy's abdomen to take just enough weight to enable the puppy to stand and walk. Repeat this little and often throughout the day. The puppy will usually be mobile in a few days. If the puppy is still not walking by four weeks, an elastic splint can be helpful. Make a figure of eight shape out of narrow elastic for both hind legs and place one of these on each leg. One loop should go above the hock and one loop below it. Link the two figures of eight with a further couple of inches of elastic to draw the legs together under the puppy. With some additional help and support the puppy should be able to walk. The splint should be used for 10 minutes at a time, four times a day. The time the splint is worn at each session can be slowly increased to 20 minutes.

If the legs splay behind the puppy despite the elastic splint, an elastic brace over the shoulders may help pull the legs under the body - see diagram. It often necessitates trying splints made from different thicknesses of elastic, until you make a splint that really helps. Do not reject the use of splints if your initial attempts fail.

ELASTIC LEG SPLINT

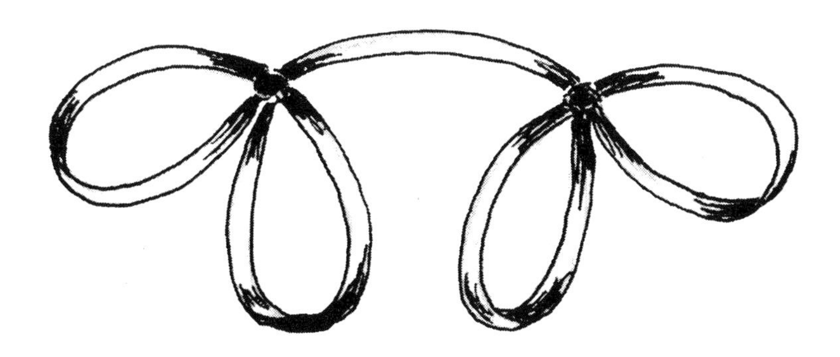

ELASTIC SPLINT WITH THORACIC SUPPORT

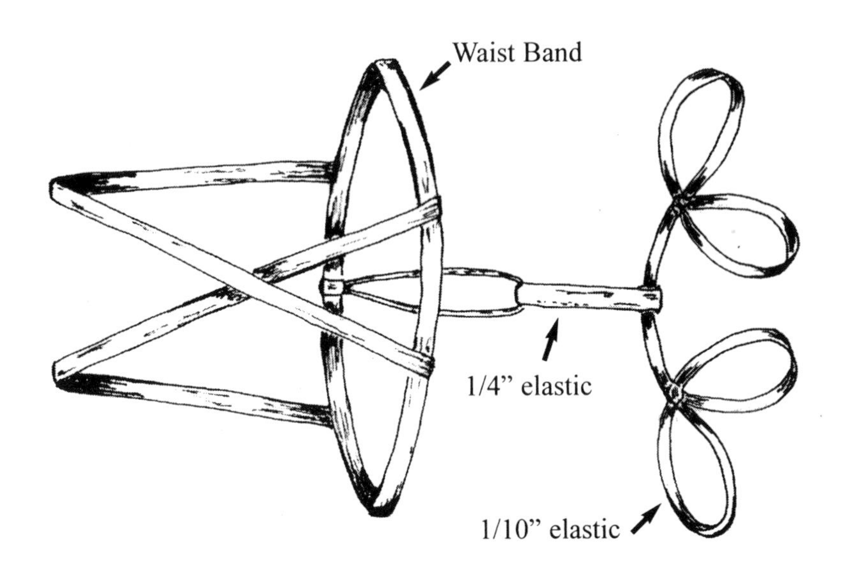

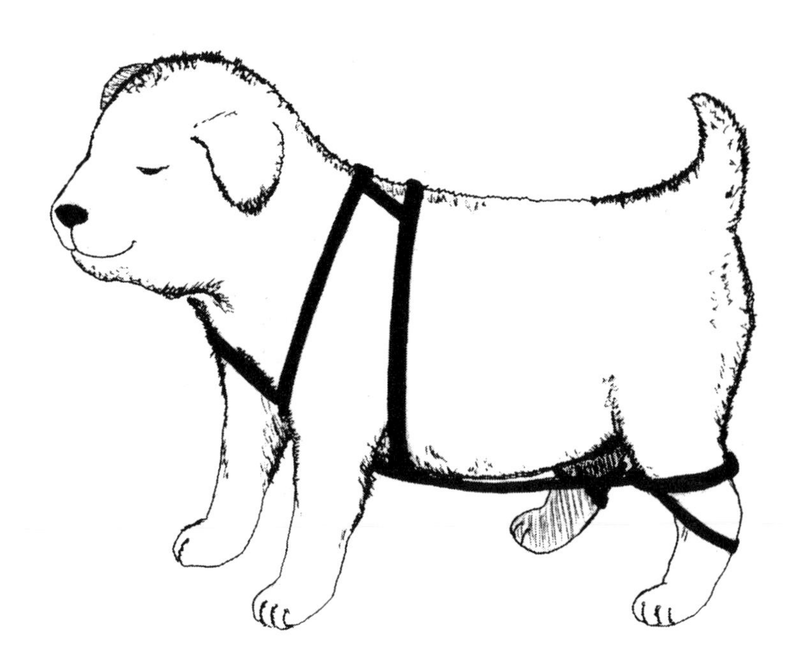

Follow-up

Never let the puppy try to move around on a slippery surface e.g. newspaper or vinyl until it has fully recovered. These puppies take a variable time to recover. The flattening of the chest gradually improves as the puppy becomes more proficient at standing.

Special Note

Please persevere with exercising the puppy - they can recover. A number of puppies who started life as swimmers have become Show Champions.

Malnutrition

This condition may occur *in utero* when a puppy does not receive adequate nutrition via the placenta. This also occurs in debilitated puppies.

Signs

These puppies are frequently small and weak. They are underweight for their size and do not gain weight as anticipated. If the puppy is hungry it may cry. As the condition of the puppy deteriorates the puppy will become weakened, and the suck reflex is also affected. Whilst it is strong enough the puppy may cry continually but it will then become less and less active. It will show the signs of hypoglycemia and dehydration. Many puppies are hypothermic and they may have diarrhoea.

Treatment

It is vital to assess the priorities. If the puppy has hypothermia this must be corrected first. Once the puppy's temperature is above 35°C (95°F) feeding can commence. Small quantities of electrolyte solution should be given every half hour (½ -1ml). If the puppy has diarrhoea this may require medication. As the puppy's condition improves the quantity of the feed can be increased and the frequency of feeds decreased. It is vital the puppy's diet should be nutritionally correct and easily digested.

Specialist Care

Precise temperature control in an incubator, reduces the stress on the puppy. If the puppy is too weak to suck it will require tube feeding. Many puppies will require specific feed mixtures, if the gut is inflamed and the puppy is unable to digest normal puppy milk mixtures. Milk feeds should not be resumed until the gut has recovered.

Special Note

If there is a problem with the maternal milk supply, the smallest, weakest puppy in the litter is usually the first to suffer. (Refer to the section on dehydration on page 40.) Other causes of malnutrition include:-

i) If the dam is receiving any drug that is being passed to the litter via her milk. Some antibiotic drugs can destroy the beneficial bacteria in the puppy's gut, so normal digestion cannot occur.

ii) Severe roundworm infection can cause malnutrition in puppies.

iii) Strong and acid milk can cause digestive problems including vomiting and colic. This should be suspected if the whole litter has similar problems. (See colic page 57.)

iv) Some medication is unsuitable for puppies and can damage the lining of the digestive tract e.g. Liquid Paraffin.

v) If a puppy has severely overshot or undershot jaws it may be unable to suck properly.

Gastritis and Vomiting

Puppies are able to vomit on a full stomach when they are about 3 days old. Vomiting is the main sign of many gastrointestinal disorders. It also occurs in megaesophagus and oesophageal obstructions (regurgitation) and some systemic disorders.

Signs

Puppies quickly become dehydrated if they continue to vomit. The quantity, consistency and colour of vomit and time after eating varies considerably and can often indicate the cause of the problem e.g. puppies that regurgitate undigested food within a few minutes of eating as soon as they start on solids may have an oesophageal obstruction. Types of vomit include:-

i) Containing food - can give guidance to how long food has remained in the stomach.

ii) Containing mucus and fluid - this can be gastric or can be swallowed salivary secretions.

iii) Yellow or green - indicates bile has entered the stomach.

iv) Fresh blood - may be small red flecks or large amounts possible with clots. This can be a sign of severe gastric infection, of an internal injury or possible blood clotting disorder.

v) "Coffee Grounds" - indicates blood that has been partially digested.

Treatment

For neonate puppies with this condition seek urgent veterinary help. To prevent the risk of dehydration, accurate diagnosis and appropriate treatment must be sought as soon as possible.

Special Care

This may be the only chance of saving very small, weak puppies. If the puppy is too young to vomit, the stomach contents should be aspirated if there is gastric dilation. These puppies frequently require fluids subcutaneously.

Diarrhoea

A puppy's motion should normally be of "toothpaste" consistency. There are many causes of diarrhoea, e.g. overfeeding, feeding an inappropriate diet, heavy worm burden and some viral and bacterial infections.

Signs

i) Loose, yellow diarrhoea is usually caused by over-feeding or the milk mixture being too rich.

ii) White stools in diarrhoea indicate the puppy has intolerance.

iii) Smelly diarrhoea is invariably caused by E. Coli infection.

Treatment

Diarrhoea causes excessive fluid and electrolyte loss, which must be replaced to prevent dehydration. If this occurs, discontinue milk feeds and give half strength electrolyte solution. Gradually re-introduce small quantities of milk as the condition improves. If, after 12 hours there is no improvement, consult your veterinary surgeon. If the diarrhoea is thought to have been caused by a rich diet, this should be reviewed. If the puppy appears to be unable to digest the current type of milk, after feeding a electrolyte solution gradually introduce a different milk mixture. These puppies may require a specific purpose food. e.g. low in lactose.

Severe Gastroenteritis

This is a serious inflammation of the stomach and intestine.

Signs

The puppy will have severe diarrhoea and may vomit. It will show obvious signs of abdominal pain. The puppy will quickly become dehydrated due to the excess loss of fluid in the faeces and vomit. If the puppy has the strength it will cry.

Treatment

The only chance to save the puppy is to obtain urgent veterinary help.

Specialist Care

This is likely to be needed. Tube feeding may then be introduced until the puppy is sufficiently strong to suck adequately for its needs. If an infection is present antibiotics may be required.

Colic

This is a condition in which gas in the stomach causes severe griping pains of the abdomen. This can be precipitated by the puppy swallowing air when nursing or bottle feeding. It can also be caused by overfeeding.

Signs

The puppy cries when touched and it will "double up" with pain. The dam can become extremely upset and agitated by the distressed puppy.

Treatment

The puppy should be removed from the nest. Treatment is aimed at easing the abdominal pain by releasing the gas.

i) Stroking the abdomen with warm damp cotton wool.

ii) Firm stroking down the spine may help the puppy to burp, releasing the gas in the stomach.

iii) Infacol, from the chemist, may provide relief (1 ml). It reduces the size of the bubbles of gas to make it easier for the puppy to release them.

When the puppy has recovered it should be fed little and often. It can be returned to the dam but it should be watched carefully and it should be burped after every meal to try and prevent a recurrence. Such a puppy may be helped by 1ml of asalone (available from chemists) half an hour before feeding.

Some puppies may require veterinary help - if the gas is not released from the stomach.

Special Note

If the entire litter is colicky, the bitch's milk is the probable cause. Strong milk and milk from a bitch on antibiotics can occasionally necessitate hand rearing of the litter. Sodium bicarbonate can be given to a bitch with acidic milk to correct this condition. This is available as a powder from most supermarkets. The powder can be dissolved into the bitch's drinking fluids. Dissolve one teaspoon to each pint of liquid, and then adjust the quantity as necessary. This may make her motions loose and affect the motions of her puppies.

Constipation

This occurs when a puppy does not pass a motion, so that faeces accumulate in the rectum and colon. This can result in the puppy becoming toxic.

Signs

This frequently occurs secondary to dehydration, as the motions become hard and lumpy. If left untreated the abdomen will become distended and feel hard. The discomfort may make the puppy cry. If a puppy is allowed to strain without passing a motion easily, prolapse of the anus can occur. Puppies must be stimulated to pass a motion after each feed.

Treatment

If the puppy is dehydrated this must be rectified without delay. A small plug of warm vaseline can be worked into the anus, which will frequently act as a gentle suppository. NEVER give liquid paraffin as this can badly irritate the intestine. It is not suitable for young puppies. Care should be taken to prevent the condition recurring.

Special Care

It may be necessary for the veterinary surgeon to administer a glycerine enema.

Special Note

Some maiden dams are reluctant to stimulate their puppies to defecate. A little honey or bovril smeared on the puppies anal area will often encourage the dam to do what is expected of her!

Prolapse of the Anus

This is the protrusion of one or more layers of the lower bowel through the anal sphincter. It is frequently caused by straining when constipated or with chronic diarrhoea.

Signs

If just lining of the rectum is prolapsed a doughnut shaped protrusion will be visible at the anus. If all the layers of the rectum are involved, a cylindrical protrusion will be visible at the anus.

Treatment

Do try to identify and rectify the cause of the prolapse, and push very gently the prolapse back in.

If this is not successful or if the condition recurs seek veterinary help as soon as possible. Surgical treatment with a purse-string suture is often necessary. Dehydration, infections etc, may need treatment first. After care will need to be discussed with your veterinary surgeon.

Artresia Ani

This is the absence of an anus. It may just be the anus that is occluded or it may involve the terminal rectum.

Signs

The obstruction of the anus results in an inability for defecation to occur. This frequently causes the abdomen to become distended, although faeces may be passed by an inappropriate orifice.

If the puppy is nursed by its dam, the condition may remain unnoticed for several weeks.

Treatment

As soon as the condition is discovered the puppy should be assessed by a veterinary surgeon. If the anus is just occluded, surgery is usually feasible - but it must be done immediately, before the puppy becomes constipated.

Prognosis

Providing the puppy survives the post-operative period the prognosis is good.

Toxacara Canis (Roundworm) Infestation

Roundworms are parasites that obtain most of their nourishment from the tissues of their host, both during the larval stage and when an adult. Puppies are born with toxocara infestation which they acquire from their dam. Dormant roundworm larvae can be found embedded in the tissues of bitches. During the second half of pregnancy the larvae become active and are able to move across the placenta to the developing puppies, where they usually lodge in their liver and lungs. In young puppies mature larvae are coughed up and swallowed. Here they develop into adult worms that produce eggs which are excreted with the puppy's motions. This can occur by the time a puppy is only 2-3 weeks old.

Both larvae and adult worms remain active in the dam until after her lactation has ceased. Additional infestation of the puppies can occur via the dam's milk, and also from ingesting eggs from their environment.

Signs

Toxocara infestations may present as respiratory and or intestinal symptoms. The severity of clinical signs depends on the worm burdens and the nutritional status of the puppy. Heavy worm burdens can cause a typical "pot-belly" appearance, persistent diarrhoea, occasionally intestinal obstruction, a dry scurvy skin and a dry starry coat.

Treatment

Healthy puppies should be wormed with a preparation recommended by your veterinary surgeon routinely at three weeks of age and as your veterinary surgeon advises.

Never worm a sick puppy except under veterinary supervision. Puppies under three weeks old can be wormed, but it must only be done after discussion with your veterinary surgeon. The worm burden of puppies can be significantly reduced by worming the bitch with fenbendazole during the last trimester of pregnancy.

Puppy Septicaemia

This is a condition in which a puppy's system is filled with harmful bacteria which it may have acquired *in utero*, during whelping or after birth. Infections can be acquired through the umbilical cord just after whelping.

Signs

Puppies with this condition have a raised temperature and their tongue and gums are a fiery red. They often keep rolling over where they lie. When they cry they make the typical "mew" type whine. Early diagnosis and prompt treatment with appropriate antibiotics are essential if the puppy is to have a chance of survival. If the condition has been acquired through the umbilical cord a small, pus filled blister may be found at the umbilical area. To treat this bathe the blister with salt water 3 times daily until the blister erupts then dust the cord with "Ster-Zac" powder after each feed until the cord drops off and the navel has healed.

Specialist Care

These puppies are critically ill, so will require tube feeding and careful temperature control.

Fading Puppy Syndrome

The name tag "Fading Puppy Syndrome" is not a disease, it is a term that is used for puppies that seem to fade away for no apparent reason within a few days of birth and although various viruses and bacteria have been implicated, in some cases, the cause is unsubstantiated.

Signs

A uterine infection often causes affected puppies to be born a few days early and the puppies are usually 2oz to 3oz underweight. They have sub-normal or high temperatures, even at this stage, and they may be hyperactive or very lethargic. They look wizen, scraggy puppies, and although they may all suck at first, they do not fill out and progress like healthy puppies. The smallest of the litter is usually the first to show signs of the progressive weakness, but by no means is this the rule and these puppies will stop suckling. The stronger puppies may live for a week or more before they too stop feeding. As the weakness increases, the puppy will lose its resilience, and often their breathing becomes more laboured often developing into pneumonia until they eventually die.

Prevention

Contact your veterinary surgeon early, who may consider taking a swab from the rectum and throat of the puppy and vagina of the bitch to aid diagnosis; if the bacteria are considered responsible, the puppy can be given appropriate antibiotics.

Specialist Care

These puppies need specialist nursing. It is essential that a normal body temperature is maintained, and adequate fluids etc., are given if they are to have any chance of survival.

Hydrocephalus - Open Fontanelle

This is a condition in which there is an excess of cerebro-spinal fluid in the skull. This is frequently associated with a failure of the fontanelle bones to fuse. In most breeds of dog these bones are normally fused at birth, but not in some of the dome headed breeds e.g. Chihuahua.

Signs

These puppies frequently do not thrive as well as the rest of the litter. Palpation of the fontanelle bones reveal they have not fused. The symptoms vary with the quantity of excess fluid in the skull. In severe cases the skull appears enlarged and the bones exceptionally thin. Excessive fluid in the ventricles of the brain will cause brain damage. In advanced cases this may cause blindness, convulsions, behaviour problems such as compulsive circling, etc.

Treatment

Puppies with minimal or no neurological symptoms may require no treatment - the fontanelle hopefully fusing during the first few weeks of life. Regular assessment of these puppies is essential. Puppies with severe brain damage should be euthanased.

Skin Lesions

There are many causes of skin lesions and these can easily become infected. Causes include:-

i) Infection of the umbilicus.
ii) Infected sites from where dew claws were removed.
iii) Damage from an over-zealous dam.
iv) Damage from siblings sucking each other.
v) Environmental damage e.g. sore pads from being nursed on an unsuitable surface.
vi) Bacterial problems.

Treatment

The wounds must be kept clean - any hair may need to be cut away around the wound to permit this. Antibiotics may be required if they are infected.

It is important to find the cause of any injury to a puppy, so that further damage can be prevented. If puppies are injured by the dam biting them, they should be removed from her, before she can do any further damage, and they should be hand-reared.

Hungry puppies frequently suck one another, causing haematoma's under the skin, this can be very serious as these areas can become infected. These puppies should be separated as soon as there is any sign of this occurring. It is advisable to nurse puppies separately when hand-rearing.

CHAPTER SIX

NUTRITIONAL REQUIREMENTS AND FEED MIXTURES

CONTENTS

NUTRITIONAL REQUIREMENTS AND FEED MIXTURES

Principles of Feeding

1. A diet should be balanced, easily digested and very nutritious.
2. Feeds should be at regular times spread evenly throughout the day and night. The number of feeds vary with the age of the puppy. As it grows it is able to consume proportionally more at one time, so the number of feeds can be reduced.
3. Any change in the diet should be made gradually.

Nutritional Requirements

Water - this is needed to replace the fluid lost in the urine and faeces, and evaporated from the lungs, tongue, etc. The water balance is a delicate mechanism.
Proteins - these are used for growth and to renew the tissues of the body. Young animals need proportionately more protein than adults for growth.
Carbohydrates - these are used to provide energy. Any surplus is stored in the body as fat.
Fats/Source of energy - Some fats are essential for normal structure and function of cells. Fats have a high calorific content and are a useful source of energy.
Vitamins - these are organic substances necessary for the body to function normally and remain healthy. Some are fat soluble e.g. Vit. A & Vit. D. Water soluble vitamins e.g. Vit. B complex tend to be associated with proteins.
Minerals - such as calcium, iron, phosphorus, sodium and potassium are important for the normal functioning and development of the puppy. Both the amount and the balance of calcium and phosphorus in the diet is important.

Milk Analysis

Each species of mammal produces milk adjusted to meet the specific needs of its own young. Milk is a complete food providing all the nourishment the young of that species requires.

The milk of a bitch is very rich, which enables the very rapid growth of puppies. Cow's milk contains less protein and fat and more lactose (milk sugar).

A comparative analysis of milk is:-

	Water	Protein	Fat	Lactose	Ash
A bitch's milk	79.8	7.5	8.3	3.7	0.7
A cow's milk	87.3	3.2	3.9	4.9	0.7

The composition of the bitches milk varies with the different stages of a lactation, so the nutritional content of the milk matches the changing requirements of the puppies as they grow and develop.

Feed Mixtures

To enable the puppy to adjust to the substitute milk when hand-rearing, this should not be fed until the puppy's digestive capability has been assessed. Start by giving a rehydration mixture. With a strong puppy milk can be introduced into the diet, diluted 50/50 with the rehydration mixture within 12-24 hours of birth. Gradually the proportion of milk can be increased until the puppy can digest full strength milk.

Milk Mixtures

The basic feed mixture recommended by the Clinic for healthy puppies is:-

4 fl ozs Carnation evaporated milk
4 fl ozs boiled water that has been cooled
1 level teaspoon of glucose
1 small egg yolk, size no. 4 (no white at all)

IMPORTANT - This is NOT for weak or sick puppies who need a specific purpose food as used at our Clinic.

Alternatively, a Puppy Milk can be fed, obtainable from a good pet shop or from a veterinary surgeon. Puppy milk substitute powder is produced by several manufacturers and these are good for hand-rearing **strong, healthy puppies**, if they are used at the manufacturer's recommended strength.

Glucose Solution

This is made by dissolving 1 level teaspoon (5 grams) of glucose powder per fluid ounce (30 mls) of boiled water that has been cooled (5 level teaspoons to a quarter of a pint of water), but should not normally be fed by itself for more than 8 hours.

Rehydration Mixtures - Glucose and Electrolyte Solutions

These are very valuable in rehydrating stressed or weak puppies. They contain glucose and mineral salts that are vital for the body to function normally. Commercial mixtures can be obtained from your veterinary surgeon e.g. "Lectade", Beechams or Waltham Electrolyte solution. Very ill puppies may require fluids by injection from a veterinary surgeon.

A home-made substitute can be made if a balanced mixture is unobtainable. This is less physiological but usually adequate:

500 mls (1 pint) boiled water - cooled
12 grms (2½ teaspoons) glucose powder
¼ teaspoon salt
Pinch of bicarbonate of soda (sodium bicarbonate)

This should be mixed thoroughly and kept in the fridge for up to 24 hours. Electrolyte solution can be fed by itself for up to 48 hours. If by then a puppy's digestive system is unable to cope with the strain of digesting full strength milk, feed electrolyte solution diluted 50/50 with the milk mixture. Gradually transfer the puppy onto full strength milk.

Natural Yoghurt

This is not given for its food value but to help restore the beneficial flora bacteria in the digestive system as these can be destroyed when antibiotics are given (use a low fat one). Depending on the size of the puppy, give ½ to 1 teaspoon of natural yogurt twice daily. Very young puppies will suck a drop from a finger.

Note Bio-yoghurt to be given only after completion of antibiotic course as the antibiotics destroy the "good" bacteria in yoghurt.

Probiotic

It is a useful alternative bio-yogurt to replace the beneficial bacteria in the digestive system. For older puppies, aged 3 to 4 weeks, it can be mixed in their feed. Request this product from your veterinary surgeon.

Foster Mothers

Fostering is more successful when rearing healthy puppies of the larger breeds than with those of the smaller breeds. Problems can occur if puppies are nursed by a dam with puppies of a different age, since the constituents of the dam's milk change as her puppies grow, also there is a risk of infection to the foster puppies as they will have very little immunity in a different environment.

CHAPTER SEVEN

FEEDING TECHNIQUES

CONTENTS

This operation should only be carried out by a Veterinary Surgeon or a qualified Veterinary Nurse - The tube inserted incorrectly will cause severe suffering and may cause the premature death of a puppy.

FEEDING TECHNIQUES

Bottle Feeding

Equipment for Bottle Feeding

BOTTLE - Very limited supplies of bottles. If the puppy is very small and weak, a Catac Sl sized teat is helpful. The Catac bottles are obtainable from pet shops. NEVER use an eye dropper or syringe to drop milk onto the tongue for routine feeding, this invariably results in milk entering the lungs which will cause aspiration pneumonia and often death. This way of feeding also causes a puppy to swallow too much air which can cause severe colic, etc.
MILTON STERILISING LIQUID and a container for sterilising the bottle and teat in.
PLASTIC BOTTLE BRUSH
BABY WIPES to keep the puppy clean and fresh. Stale food left on the coat can remove the hair. (Use damp cotton wool around the muzzle.)
SOFT BRUSH for the puppy's coat.
WHITE COTTON WOOL
BOX OF TISSUES OR A ROLL OF KITCHEN PAPER TOWEL for mopping up.
SUDOCREM (from the chemist) Apply a smear after the puppy has 'performed' and has been cleaned up to prevent soreness.
BOX to keep the equipment in.
TOWEL for your lap.
GLASS SCREW-JAR (not plastic) to keep the prepared feed in.
FINE PLASTIC OR NYLON TEA-STRAINER
A BABY'S BOTTLE WARMER or a BEAKER of warm water to stand the bottle in, to keep the feed warm.
ABIDEC multi-vitamin drops (from the pharmacy).
STER-ZAC POWDER for the puppy's cord (from the pharmacy).
ALARM CLOCK Regular feeding is very important with newborn puppies.

All the equipment must be kept very clean to minimise the risk of infection. The bottle and teat should be thoroughly cleaned between each feed and sterilised in Milton Solution. This solution must be changed every day. Rub the teat inside and out with a little salt, as this removes the particles of milk solids that can adhere to the teat. Rinse thoroughly in cold water, before placing in the Milton Solution. Unless all particles are removed from the bottle and teat the Milton Solution may not be fully effective. Before use the teat and bottle must be removed from the sterilising solution and rinsed very thoroughly to remove all traces of the solution.

How To Get The Hole In The Teat

This often causes problems. Be very careful and nick a tiny hole with a pair of small, very fine, sterilised nail scissors. When the bottle is pointed down a slow drip is the correct result. Too small a hole means the puppy will exhaust itself, getting very little, or nothing. Too large a hole means that the mixture may be inhaled resulting in aspiration pneumonia, so the puppy will develop pneumonia, or if the puppy feeds too quickly the puppy may develop colic or wind.

Prepare the Feed

Mix the ingredients together, then strain through the nylon tea strainer two or three times. Pour it into a sterilised glass screw top jar to cool. When cold put it in the refrigerator where it will keep for 24 hours. Always shake the jar containing the feed before you use it to ensure that it is well mixed. Slowly warm the amount of milk needed for the feed to 36°C (96.8°F). A bottle warmer is the safest way to warm the feed.

NOTE: It is very dangerous to use a microwave for reheating the milk because of overheating - and of heating it too quickly.

Method of Feeding

Fill the bottle to the correct amount required for the feed and check the temperature of the milk on the underside of your wrist. Then sit down comfortably with the towel on your lap. Have everything you need within reach, including your box of equipment and the milk feed. Before you start gently stroke the puppy's tummy with a warm cotton wool ball to help it urinate, which it will need to do if it has just woken up.

Place the puppy on your lap, do not hold it from underneath; some puppies are happier feeding on their sides. With the thumb and forefinger (preferably of the hand that's holding the puppy), GENTLY squeeze the corners of the mouth which will cause the mouth to open. Gently place the teat in, then check the tongue is under the teat and not in the roof of the mouth. If it is correctly positioned the tongue will close around the teat and form a seal. This is necessary for the puppy to suck properly. (The same applies if you are holding the puppy onto the mother.)

If the puppy will not suck, despite the teat being correctly positioned, gently stroke the throat to encourage sucking. With a very tiny puppy that is not co-operating, gently stroke the muzzle on either side of the nose, again, this encourages sucking.

If the puppy is strong, and especially if it is greedy, it should be given half of the feed, then be winded (burped) before it is given the rest of the feed. Wind the puppy again when it has finished feeding. To wind a puppy tilt its head up with your thumb and forefinger. With the other hand gently rub back towards the tail.

Once a day give 'Abidec' vitamin drops onto the front of the tongue. One drop should be given once a day for the first week then 2-3 drops a day until the puppy is a month old.

NOTE: Do not give these drops if using a milk formula containing added vitamins.

Amount to Feed

With a strong puppy, about 6ozs body weight, give approximately a teaspoon (5ml) per feed EVERY TWO HOURS, not longer, DAY AND NIGHT, for the first fourteen days from birth, (about 60ml in total per 24 hours). Gradually increase the amount fed and the time between feeds as the puppy grows from 14 days.

Toileting

After every feed use a warm damp cotton wool ball to stimulate the puppy to urinate and pass a motion by gently stroking the puppy's genital and anal regions. This must be done to keep the puppy healthy. If the puppy does not pass a motion when you stroke the anal area firmly try dabbing the anus with the warm cotton wool. If a motion is not passed for 12 hours an enema must be given, but only by a veterinary surgeon/veterinary nurse. Clean the puppy, taking care to wipe any spilt feed off its coat. Do not use baby wipes around the mouth. Dry the puppy, and smear 'Sudocrem' around the genital and anal areas to prevent soreness and urine burn. Dust the navel area with 'Ster-Zac' powder. Put the puppy back to rest.

Restlessness

If this occurs after an apparently normal feed it may be because the puppy has wind. Other causes include the puppy being too hot or too cold. If the puppy has colic it will be distressed.

Records

After each feed record on a chart:-

i) The time the feed was given.
ii) The type of feed and the quantity given.
iii) If the puppy urinates record any abnormality in colour or quantity.
iv) If the puppy passes a motion - record any abnormality in the consistency such as being loose, creamy or curdy.
v) Comment on any change in the puppy's behaviour.

Such records do not take long to do and can be very helpful to monitor any changes in a puppy's condition, and may be helpful for future reference.

Weighing

Accurate weighing is essential to monitor the progress of the puppy. Digital scales are the most accurate, but scales used to weigh food for people on diets are useful. All puppies should be weighed at birth. Weigh the puppy daily for the first week of life, then weigh them on alternate days. It is important to weigh the puppy at the same time of day. A careful record should be kept of the weights. A normal healthy puppy nursing on the bitch should gain ½ - loz. in the first 48 hours. Ideally a healthy puppy should double it's birth weight by seven to ten days of age. Hand reared puppies must be expected to gain weight at a slower rate.

Emergency Feeding for Puppies Without Suck Reflex

Many weak puppies have been saved by taking advantage of the fact that glucose is easily absorbed directly through the roof of the mouth. Ensure you keep the puppy warm - feed glucose solution, by dipping your little finger in the solution and gently stroking this first on the roof of the mouth then stroke it on the front of the tongue. This needs to be continued very gently for 5-10 minutes. Give the puppy a rest and then resume in another 20 minutes. This is very time consuming - a real labour of love - but it can work, and has helped many puppies survive.

Dropper Feeding

This can also save the life of a puppy without a suck reflex. There is a great risk of milk being inhaled, which can cause aspiration pneumonia, so it must be done very slowly and carefully.

Keep the puppy's head well forward, and place a small single drop on the front of the tongue. Repeat this VERY SLOWLY one drop at a time.

Tube Feeding

Please do not try to do this unless you have been carefully taught by someone experienced in this procedure. Without practical experience and the correct equipment this method of feeding can be fatal, if the gastric tube is misplaced and enters the lungs, the result will cause irreversible damage to the puppy - and more often than not the puppy will not survive.

To do this safely it is essential to have the correct equipment:-

i) **A 5ml syringe** for feeding small puppies and a 10ml one for older puppies.

ii) **A feeding tube**. For the newborn puppies of toy breeds I use catheters, sizes 3FG to 6FG.

iii) **A stethoscope**.

The tube must be carefully measured to fit the puppy. Lay the tube against the puppy. Place the tip of the tube approximately ¾ of the way along the ribs and measure carefully to the mouth. Mark this point with micropore tape so that you know how far to insert the tube. The tube should be remeasured regularly so that it can be lengthened as the puppy grows.

To feed the puppy gently squeeze the corners of the mouth to open it and carefully pass the tube over the back of the tongue and gently ease it down the throat. The other hand should hold the puppy's head still throughout the whole procedure. If any resistance is felt when passing the tube it should be withdrawn carefully as the tube will have gone into the lungs. Any feed given would drown the puppy and result in death.

When you have inserted the tube so that the marker is at the puppy's mouth, listen to the free end of the tube with your stethoscope. If you hear wheezing, bubbling sounds the tube is in the lungs, so holding the head still, withdraw the tube gently and try again.

Only when you are absolutely certain that you have got the tube in the stomach, check the temperature of the feed and see that the syringe containing it does not contain any air. Attach the syringe to the end of the tube. Depress the plunger slowly and smoothly. It should take ½ -1 minute to complete giving the feed. Wait a few seconds before removing the tube. Keep the puppy steady throughout the procedure.

The care given to the puppy after the feed is the same as after bottle feeding.

The syringe and tube must be carefully cleaned after every feed, and then place them in a solution of Milton.

CHAPTER EIGHT

WEANING

CONTENTS

Weaning

This is the term given to the process of gradually transferring a puppy from a liquid diet, normally milk, to a more solid diet.

The diet needs to be balanced, palatable and easily digested. It must have a high protein content to provide the materials for the puppy's rapid growth, as well as providing the energy for the puppy's activity and body maintenance.

It is important to prevent set backs occurring during the growing period as these can prevent a puppy achieving its full growth potential. This is especially important with puppies who have had problems early in life, since they are often much smaller than normal at weaning time.

Every effort should be made to avoid putting the digestive system under stress as this often causes diarrhoea. Common causes include sudden changes in the diet, over feeding or feeding a diet that is not easily digested. Very occasionally an individual puppy may have an allergy to a specific food but this is uncommon. The small size of a puppy's stomach means the food should be divided into small meals spread equally throughout the day. Regular food times also help reduce digestive upsets.

The quantity of food a puppy needs varies with the different breeds, but can be two or three times the quantity required by an adult dog of the same size. If a diet is adequate this will be reflected in the general condition of the puppy, the condition of its faeces and its weight gain. Knowledge of the average weight of puppies in your specific breed is a useful guide to a puppy's progress. A healthy puppy should be fit and active. Overfeeding encourages a puppy to become fat and lethargic and can result in various orthopaedic problems particularly in the larger breeds. Fat puppies are likely to become obese adults unless the owner takes steps to rectify the condition.

Dog breeders have very different views on the best type of diet to feed. Many advocate a complete manufactured diet as this is the most reliable to provide a balanced diet. Other breeders prefer to use a home-made traditional diet incorporating a large proportion of fresh foods. Care is needed to ensure such a diet is fully balanced (but it can be 'tailor-made') to meet the specific requirements of your own breed. Variety does add to the animals interest in food. Most breeders feed a mixed diet incorporating a proportion of manufactured foods in their feeding plan.

The transfer of a puppy onto more solid food must be done gradually to allow the puppy's digestive system to adapt. The age breeders begin weaning and the first type food fed varies considerably. Puppies can be taught to lap by about 2½ weeks. Other breeders prefer to start weaning by introducing a small quantity of scraped beef once the puppy is about three weeks old. Both systems are successful providing they are done with care.

When a puppy has learnt to lap and is having small quantities of meat, other food can be introduced into the diet, but only add a maximum of one new type of food in any 24-48 hour period. New stresses on puppies should be limited to a maximum of one a day. Such care is rewarded by the ease in which a puppy adapts to each new situation. If a problem does occur this makes it much easier to identify the cause.

Multivitamin and Mineral Supplements

These are not necessary if a complete balanced food containing adequate vitamins and minerals are fed. If a home-made traditional diet is fed the puppy should be given a complete vitamin supplement every day e.g. Canovel. NEVER exceed the quantity recommended by the manufacturers.

Teaching Puppies To Lap

Most puppies can learn to lap by about 2½ weeks old. It is easier for puppies to lap a semi-solid food so a little baby rice, e.g. Farex should be mixed with the milk. With hand reared puppies use the normal milk formula slightly thickened. Always use the same brand of baby rice, mixed with the same type of puppy milk. Place a small quantity of the mixture in a shallow bowl. Dip your finger in the mixture and allow the puppy to lick it. Repeat this, slowly lowering your finger into the mixture. Most puppies learn to lap quickly - some blow bubbles at first, but with patience it does not take long to teach them. The puppies are very messy at first and need careful cleaning after feeding.

Scraped Beef

The Clinic advises that beef should be scraped before being fed to tiny puppies. Lay a piece of raw beef on a board. With a sharp knife angled away from you, scrape the cut surface of the meat. The pulp will accumulate on the blade of the knife. This should be rolled into a small ¼ inch diameter ball for each puppy.

Meat should be fed to puppies individually to ensure each receives its share, and to prevent a puppy being given too much. Hold the "meat ball" between your thumb and first finger and allow the puppy to suck and lick it. Virtually all puppies love the taste and quickly start to eat. After hand reared puppies have had their meat they should be given a drink of puppy milk to complete the feed.

After a couple of days giving meat once a day a second meat meal may be added. Only after a further day or so should the quantity fed be gradually increased. Puppies especially large and giant breeds have exacting calcium requirements. Too little or too much calcium can cause bone problems. **NEVER** risk using pet mince for the weaning of young puppies. The risks to the puppy's health cannot justify any financial saving.

Care: Scraped beef is extremely deficient in calcium and a balanced diet should be introduced as soon as possible such as HILL'S SCIENCE DIET CANINE GROWTH.

At the Clinic

We have tried to find a weaning regime that is easy for the owners of puppies to continue at home. We supply a "Going Home Diet" for the owner to continue with the Clinic's dietary advice for each particular puppy.

Feeding Plan for Sturdy Puppies

At two weeks give 9 feeds spread evenly throughout the 24 hours.
By three weeks give 7 feeds spread from 6 a.m. to midnight.
By four weeks give 6 feeds spread from 7 a.m. to 11 p.m.
By five weeks give 5 feeds spread from 7 a.m. to 11 p.m.
By seven to eight weeks give 4 feeds spread from 7 a.m. to 11 p.m.

IN CONCLUSION

The first puppy I saved was my own little sable and white Sheltie called 'Dee-Dee' and to whose memory this book is dedicated. She lived a full happy life for fifteen years, and had many notable obedience wins. She convinced me that all the time and effort it takes to save these puppies is worthwhile, providing they are able to lead normal happy lives. The number of puppies one can save and their ultimate quality depends so much on how carefully they are hand reared. I feel that all of the work is justified every time I see puppies, that would otherwise have died, grow into strong healthy adults.

Our grateful thanks go to Her Highness Princess Antoinette of Monaco, who, following a meeting with the Princess three years ago, gave me an added incentive to continue with the clinic and to give help and advice where it was needed.

As a friend and valued contributor I am very grateful to Adrienne Hughes for committing my ideas to paper.

I can never thank my veterinary surgeons adequately for all the help and support they give me, in particular to Sarah Wilkins BV.Sc., M.R.C.V.S for her time and dedicated veterinary skills and for her time and advice in connection with this book.

As the good name of the clinic has been greeted by dog breeders throughout the UK so has its reputation with large organisations who provide dogs with food and nutrition, to these people my thanks for your support and understanding, in particular Dr. Richard Butterwick BSc.PhD. of Waltham Pet Centre for his personal interest shown in the Clinic.

There are numerous people and organisations in the "Doggy" world, too many to name individually, who with their fund raising efforts, enables the Clinic to progress with its work.

A special thank you to Margaret Crispin and indeed Hill's Pet Nutrition Ltd for supporting and arranging publication of this guide to hand rearing, for without their help this would not have been possible.

A final thank you to my husband, Chris and my daughter Samantha, for your support in my venture.